The Chemical Dependence Treatment Planner

Robert R. Perkinson

Arthur E. Jongsma, Jr.

JOHN WILEY & SONS, INC.

New York • Chichester • Weinheim • Brisbane • Singapore • Toronto

This book is printed on acid-free paper. ⊚

Copyright © 1998 by Robert R. Perkinson and Arthur E. Jongsma, Jr.
All rights reserved.
Published by John Wiley & Sons, Inc.
Published simultaneously in Canada.

Library of Congress Cataloging-in-Publication Data

Perkinson, Robert R.
    The chemical dependence treatment planner / by Robert R.
Perkinson, Arthur E. Jongsma, Jr.
        p.   cm.
    Includes index.
    ISBN 0-471-23795-7 (pbk. : alk. paper). — ISBN 0-471-23794-9
(pbk./disk : alk. paper)
      1. Substance abuse—Treatment—Handbooks, manuals, etc.
   2. Substance abuse—Treatment—Planning.   I. Jongsma, Arthur E.,
1943– . II. Title.
RC564.15.P47   1998
616.86'06—dc21   97-35792
                                                                CIP

Printed in the United States of America

10 9 8 7 6 5

CONTENTS

INTRODUCTION

HISTORICAL BACKGROUND

Over the past 30 years, formalized treatment planning has gradually become an integral component of the entire health care delivery system—including behavioral health and substance abuse treatment. Treatment planning started in the medical sector in the 1960s and spread into the mental health sector in the 1970s, as clinics, inpatient facilities, and agencies began to seek accreditation from bodies such as the Joint Commission on Accreditation of Healthcare Organizations (JCAHO). In order for treatment facilities to achieve accreditation, it was necessary for the staff providers to strengthen their clinical documentation skills—particularly in terms of creating quantifiable treatment plans tailored to the needs of each patient.

With the advent of managed care in the 1980s, treatment planning expanded from inpatient settings to partial hospitalization, day treatment programs, and outpatient settings. Managed care systems require that clinicians move rapidly from assessment of the problem to the formulation and implementation of the treatment plan. Once formulated, these treatment plans can help keep the provider and the patient focused on the purpose of treatment—and help catalyze progress toward change. In order to fulfill this role, each patient's treatment plan must be:

1. Specific as to the problems and interventions
2. Individualized to meet the particular patient's needs and goals
3. Measurable in terms of setting milestones that can be used to chart the patient's progress and assess treatment outcome

TREATMENT PLAN UTILITY

Detailed, measurable, written treatment plans can benefit not only the patient, but also the provider, the treatment team, the insurance community, the treatment agency, and the overall substance abuse treatment profession.

Patient Benefits

The treatment plan provides a road map for the patient to follow on his or her journey through treatment. This road map helps to point the way and focus the journey. It is very easy for both provider and patient to lose sight of the issues that brought the patient into therapy. The treatment plan serves to structure the focus of the therapeutic contract. However, issues can change as therapy progresses, and the treatment plan must be viewed as a dynamic document that can and must be updated to reflect any major change of problem, definition, goal, objective, or intervention.

Both patients and therapists benefit as the treatment plan forces them to think about treatment outcomes. Clear behavioral objectives allow the patient to channel effort into specific changes that will lead to the long-term goal of problem resolution. Treatment is no longer a vague contract that simply allows the patient to talk openly until he or she feels better. Instead, both patient and therapist can concentrate on working toward discrete objectives using clearly stated interventions.

Provider Benefits

Providers are aided by treatment plans because such plans compel the clinician to think analytically and critically about which therapeutic interventions are best suited to achieve the objectives for a particular patient. The therapist must give advance attention to the technique, approach, assignment, or cathartic target that will form the basis for interventions.

Clinicians also benefit from clear documentation of treatment because it provides added protection from a disgruntled patient's litigation. Malpractice suits are increasing in frequency, and liability insurance premiums are soaring. The first line of defense against allegations is a complete clinical record that details the treatment process. A written, individualized treatment plan, which has been reviewed and signed by the patient, coupled with contemporaneous, problem-oriented progress notes, is a powerful defense against exaggerated or false claims.

Treatment Team Benefits

Treatment plans also provide an important means of communication for treatment teams. This is particularly important in chemical dependency treatment settings because a multitude of clinicians (e.g., psychiatrist, medical doctor, psychologist, nursing staff, psychotherapist, substance abuse counselor) may well simultaneously or consecutively work with the patient. The treatment plan can help to provide continuity as the patient works with each of these providers and moves through the chemical dependence continuum of care. Most accrediting and regulatory bodies now require specificity as to who is responsible for providing each intervention. In this *Planner,* there is a space marked RP (Responsible Professional) to indicate the provider handling each intervention. Users may also employ the blank lines to designate the professional degree and/or discipline of the RP (for example, Tracey Jones, M.D., attending psychiatrist; Alex Smith, B.S., Substance Abuse Counselor). By clearly delineating the objectives, treatment approaches, and party responsible for each intervention, treatment plans and progress notes foster effective communication among team members.

Treatment Center Benefits

Substance abuse treatment centers and behavioral health care agencies constantly seek ways to increase the quality and uniformity of the documentation in the clinical record. Adding a standardized, written treatment plan (including problem definitions, goals, objectives, and interventions) to every patient's file enhances that uniformity of documentation. This eases the task of record reviewers both inside and outside the agency. Outside reviewers such as JCAHO insist on documentation that clearly outlines assessment, treatment, progress, and discharge status.

The demand for accountability from third-party payers and HMOs is partially satisfied by a written treatment plan and complete progress notes. More and more managed care systems are demanding a structured therapeutic contract that has measurable objectives and explicit interventions. Clinicians are increasingly accountable to those outside the treatment process.

Benefits to the Substance Abuse Treatment Profession

The substance abuse treatment profession stands to benefit from the use of more precise, measurable objectives to evaluate success in treatment. Measurable objectives facilitate the collection of outcome data regarding interventions that are effective in achieving specific objectives. Treatment planning computer software has been published to assist in creating a treatment plan and to track patient progress, analyzing and graphing outcome data (Jongsma, Peterson, and McInnis, 1997).

HOW TO DEVELOP A TREATMENT PLAN

The process of developing a treatment plan involves a logical series of steps that build on one another. The foundation of any effective treatment plan is the data gathered in a thorough biopsychosocial assessment. As the patient presents him- or herself for treatment, the clinician must listen sensitively to understand the patient's struggles, not only in terms of a chemical dependency problem, but also in terms of the surrounding family-of-origin issues, current stressors, emotional status, social network, physical health, coping skills, interpersonal conflicts, self-esteem, and so on. It is important to assess the impact of the substance abuse on all of the major dimensions of the patient's life: work, recreation, intimate relationships, finances, legal involvement, physical health, extended family relationships, and so forth. The assessment should probe the ways in which these factors have contributed to substance abuse, as well as the biochemical influence of genetic vulnerability to chemical dependency. Assessment data may be gathered from a social history, physical exam, clinical interview, psychological testing, or contact with a patient's significant others. The integration of the data by the clinician or the multidisciplinary treatment team members is critical for understanding the patient. Once the assessment is complete, use the following six steps to develop a treatment plan.

Step One: Problem Selection

This *Chemical Dependence Planner* offers treatment plan components for 29 behavioral and psychological problems often associated with chemical dependency. Although there may be a number of co-morbid problems that surface during the initial assessment, the clinician must ferret out the most significant issues. Usually a *primary* problem (e.g., Substance Abuse/Dependence) will surface, and *secondary* problems (e.g., Impulsivity, Borderline Traits) may also be evident. Some *other* problems may have to be set aside as not urgent enough to require concurrent treatment. An effective treatment plan can deal with only a few selected problems, or treatment will lose its direction.

In choosing the problems on which to focus, it is important to note both those problems that are most acute or disruptive to the patient's functioning and those concerns that are most important to the patient. The patient's motivation to participate in and cooperate with the treatment process depends, to some extent, on the degree to which treatment addresses his or her greatest needs.

Step Two: Problem Definition

Each individual patient uniquely reveals how a problem behaviorally manifests itself in his or her life. Therefore, each problem that is selected for treatment must be defined in its relation to the particular patient. The symptom pattern should be associated with diagnostic criteria and codes such as those found in the *Diagnostic and Statistical Manual* or the *International Classification of Diseases.* The *Chemical Dependence Planner,* following the pattern established by DSM-IV, offers an array of behaviorally specific problem definition statements. Each of the 29 presenting problems has several behavioral symptoms from which to choose. These prewritten definitions may also be used as models to craft additional definitions.

Step Three: Goal Development

The next step in treatment plan development is to set broad goals aimed at replacing dysfunctional behaviors with adaptive ones in order to facilitate resolution of the target problem(s). Goals need not be crafted in measurable terms, but instead should focus on the long-term, global outcomes of treatment. (Goals and Objectives are often confused in treatment plans. Arnold Goldman suggests using the "see Johnny test" to distinguish the two components. That is, if you can see Johnny do something [e.g., read the *Big Book* of Alcoholics Anonymous], then it is an objective; if you can't see Johnny do it [e.g., improve self-esteem] then it is a goal.) Although the *Chemical Dependence Planner* suggests several possible goal statements for each problem, it is necessary to select only one goal for each identified problem.

Step Four: Objective Construction

As illustrated by the "see Johnny test," in contrast to long-term goals, objectives must be stated in behaviorally measurable language. The point at which the patient has achieved the established objectives must be clear. Review agencies (e.g., JCAHO), HMOs, and managed care organizations insist that treatment results be measurable. The objectives presented in this *Chemical Dependence Planner* are designed to meet this demand for accountability. Numerous alternatives are presented to allow construction of a variety of treatment plan possibilities for the same presenting problem. The clinician must exercise professional judgment to establish which objectives are most appropriate for a given patient.

Each objective should be developed as a step toward attaining the broad treatment goal. In essence, objectives can be thought of as a series of steps that, when completed, will result in the achievement of the long-term goal. There should be at least two objectives for each problem, but the clinician may construct as many as are necessary for goal achievement. Target attainment dates should be listed for each objective. New objectives should be added to the plan as the individual's treatment progresses. Achieving all the necessary objectives should signal resolution of the patient's target problem and attainment of the written goal.

Step Five: Intervention Creation

Interventions are actions of the clinician designed to help the patient complete the objectives. There should be at least one intervention for every objective. If the patient does not accomplish the objective after the initial intervention, new interventions should be added to the plan.

Interventions should be selected on the basis of the patient's needs and the provider team's full treatment repertoire. This *Chemical Dependence Treatment Planner* contains interventions from a broad range of treatment modalities (group therapy, individual therapy, occupational therapy, etc.) as well as an array of therapeutic approaches, including cognitive, dynamic, behavioral, pharmacological, family-oriented, experiential/expressive, solution-focused brief therapy, and 12-step-oriented (the exercises used in the *Planner* are available in one volume in *Chemical Dependency Counseling: A Practical Guide,* by Robert R. Perkinson, published by Sage Publications, Thousand Oaks, California, or one at a time from the Hazelden Foundation, located in Center City Minnesota).

Step Six: Diagnosis Determination

The determination of an appropriate diagnosis is based on an evaluation of the patient's complete clinical presentation. The clinician must compare the behavioral, cognitive, emotional, and interpersonal symptoms that the patient presents to the criteria for diagnosis of a mental illness as described in DSM-IV. Careful assessment of behavioral indicators facilitates more accurate diagnosis and more effective treatment planning. *The Chemical Dependence Treatment Planner* has some suggestions for DSM-IV diagnoses (used with permission from American Psychiatric Press, Inc.) for each problem, but the clinician must use his or her professional training and judgment to make a final diagnostic determination.

HOW TO USE THIS *PLANNER*

Learning the skills of effective treatment plan writing can be a tedious and difficult process for many clinicians. The documentation demands can be overwhelming when each clinician must coordinate with myriad providers. Because the process must move rapidly from assessment to treatment plan to intervention to progress reporting, *The Chemical Dependence Treatment Planner* was developed as a tool to aid clinicians in quickly writing treatment plans that are clear, specific, and highly individualized. Each plan should be developed by moving, in turn, through each of the following steps:

1. Choose one presenting problem (Step One) from those identified in the assessment process. Locate the corresponding page number for that problem in the *Chemical Dependence Planner*'s table of contents.
2. Select two or three of the listed behavioral definitions (Step Two) and record them (or modify them as necessary) in the appropriate section on the treatment plan form.
3. Select a single long-term goal (Step Three) and record it in the Goals section of the treatment plan form.
4. Review the listed objectives for this problem and select the ones clinically indicated for the patient (Step Four). Remember, it is recommended that at least two objectives be selected for each problem. Add a target date or the number of sessions allocated for the attainment of each objective.
5. Choose relevant interventions (Step Five). *The numbers of the interventions most salient to each objective are listed in parentheses following the objective statement.* Feel free to choose other interventions from the list or to add new interventions as needed in the space provided. If the treatment is being carried out by a multidisciplinary team, note the Responsible Provider after each intervention by name, degree, and discipline/title.

6. DSM-IV diagnoses commonly associated with the problem are listed at the end of each chapter. These diagnoses are suggestions for clinical consideration. Select a diagnosis listed or assign a more appropriate choice from the DSM-IV (Step Six).

   Note: To accommodate those practitioners who tend to plan treatment in terms of diagnostic labels rather than presenting problems, the appendix lists all of the DSM-IV diagnoses that are included in the *Planner,* cross-referenced to the Problems related to each diagnosis.

Following these steps will facilitate the development of a complete, individualized treatment plan, ready for immediate implementation and presentation to the patient. The final plan should resemble the format of the sample plan presented at the end of this Introduction.

ELECTRONIC TREATMENT PLANNING

Many care facilities rely on computerized record keeping. The presenting problems, goals, objectives, interventions, and diagnoses in *The Chemical Dependence Treatment Planner* are available in electronic form as an add-on upgrade module to the popular software *Thera-Scribe® 3.0 for Windows®: The Computerized Assistant to Psychotherapy Treatment Planning.* For more information on *TheraScribe* or *The Chemical Dependence Treatment Planner* add-on module, call John Wiley & Sons at 1-800-879-4539, or mail in the information request coupon at the back of this book.

A WORD OF CAUTION

Whether using the print version *Planner* or the electronic version (*TheraScribe*), it is critical to remember that effective treatment planning requires tailoring each plan to the individual patient's problems and needs. *Treatment plans should not be mass-produced, even if patients have similar problems.* The individual's strengths and weaknesses, unique stressors, social network, family circumstances, and symptom patterns *must* be considered in developing a treatment strategy. The clinically derived statements in this *Planner* can be combined in thousands of permutations to develop detailed treatment plans. In addition, readers are encouraged add their own definitions, goals, objectives, and interventions to the existing samples.

SAMPLE TREATMENT PLAN

Problem: RELAPSE-PRONE

Definitions: Patient has a history of multiple treatment attempts and relapse.
Friends or family members are substance abusers.
Patient has never worked on a program of recovery long enough to maintain abstinence.

Goals: Reduce the risk for relapse and maintain a program of recovery free of substance abuse.
Develop a new peer group supportive of recovery.
Develop coping skills to use when experiencing high-risk situations and/or craving.

Objectives

1. Write a detailed chemical-use history describing treatment attempts and the specific situations surrounding relapse (2/12/98).

2. Verbalize an acceptance of powerlessness over alcohol/drugs (2/15/98).

3. Visit physician to see if pharmacological intervention is warranted, and take all medication as directed (2/24/98).

4. List five reasons for patient's failure to work on a daily program of recovery (2/18/98).

Interventions

1. Have the patient write a chemical-use history describing his/her attempts at recovery. Teach the patient the high risk situations (e.g., negative emotions, social pressure, interpersonal conflict, positive emotions, testing personal control) that lead to relapse.
   RP: Molly Evans, M.A.
   Substance Abuse Counselor

2. Using an AA step one exercise, help the patient see the powerlessness and unmanageability that result from substance abuse and relapse.
   RP: Molly Evans, M.A.
   Substance Abuse Counselor

3. Physician will examine the patient, order medications as indicated, titrate medications, and monitor for side effects.
   RP: Dwight Kessler, M.D.
   Psychiatrist

4. Using a relapse history, help the patient understand the reasons he/she failed to work on a program of recovery.
   RP: Molly Evans, M.A.
   Substance Abuse Counselor

(Continued)

5. Write a plan to increase reinforcement when attending
recovery group meetings
(2/20/98).

5. Help the patient develop a
plan that will increase the
rewards obtained at recovery
groups (e.g., concentrate on
helping others, go for dessert
after the meeting, socialize,
stick with the winners).
RP: John Smith, Psy.D.
      Group Therapy Leader

6. Develop a written plan to deal
with each high-risk situation
(e.g., negative emotions,
social pressure, interpersonal
conflict, positive emotions,
testing personal control)
(2/22/98).

6. Help the patient develop a
written continuing care plan
that includes the essential
elements necessary for him/
her to maintain abstinence
and continue recovery.
RP: Molly Evans, M.A.
      Substance Abuse Counselor

7. Practice alcohol/drug refusal
skills (2/22/98).

7. Use modeling, role playing,
and behavior rehearsal to
teach the patient how to say
no to alcohol/drugs; then
practice refusal in several
high-risk situations.
RP: Molly Evans, M.A.
      Substance Abuse Counselor

8. Make a card of emergency phone
numbers to call for help in a
high-risk situation (2/25/98).

8. Help the patient make an
emergency card to carry at all
times that has the phone
numbers of people to call in
high-risk situations.
RP: Molly Evans, M.A.
      Substance Abuse Counselor

9. Develop a written personal
recovery plan (e.g., be honest,
regularly attend recovery group
meetings, get a sponsor, and
seek any other treatment
needed to maintain abstinence)
(2/25/98).

9. Help the patient decide
on the aftercare placement
that is structured enough
to help him/her maintain
abstinence (e.g., halfway
house, group home, out-
patient treatment, day care,
partial hospitalization).
RP: Molly Evans, M.A.
      Substance Abuse Counselor

Diagnosis: 303.90 Alcohol Dependence

ADULT CHILD OF
AN ALCOHOLIC TRAITS

BEHAVIORAL DEFINITIONS

1. A history of being raised in an alcoholic home that resulted in having experienced emotional abandonment, role confusion, abuse, and a chaotic, unpredictable environment.
2. Inability to trust others, share feelings, or talk openly about self.
3. Overly concerned with the welfare of other people.
4. Passively submissive to the wishes, wants, and needs of others; too eager to please others.
5. Chronically fearful of interpersonal abandonment and desperately clings to destructive relationships.
6. Tells other people what they want to hear rather than the truth.
7. Persistent feelings of worthlessness and a belief that being treated with disdain is normal and expected.
8. Strong feelings of panic and helplessness when faced with being alone as a close relationship ends.
9. Chooses partners and friends who are chemically dependent or have other serious problems.
10. Distrusts authority figures—trusts only peers.
11. Takes on the parental role in a relationship.
12. Feels less worthy than those who had a more normal family life.
13. Chronic feelings of alienation from others.

__. _____
   _____

__. _____
   _____
   _____

__. _____
   _____

LONG-TERM GOALS

1. Recover from substance abuse that reduces the impact of adult child of an alcoholic (ACOA) traits on sobriety.
2. Decrease dependence on relationships while beginning to meet his or her own needs, build confidence, and practice assertiveness.
3. Demonstrate healthy communication that is honest, open, and self-disclosing.
4. Recognize adult child of an alcoholic traits and their detrimental effects on recovery.
5. Reduce the frequency of behaviors exclusively designed to please others.
6. Demonstrate the ability to recognize, accept, and meet the needs of self.
7. Replace negative, self-defeating thinking with self-enhancing messages to self.
8. Choose partners and friends who are responsible, respectful, and reliable.
9. Overcome fears of abandonment, loss, and neglect as the source of these feelings (being raised in an alcoholic home) becomes clear.
10. Reduce feelings of alienation by learning similarity to others who were raised in a more normal home.
11. Improve feelings of self-worth by helping others in recovery.

—. _____

_____

—. _____

_____

—. _____

_____

SHORT-TERM OBJECTIVES

1. Acknowledge the feelings of powerlessness that result from ACOA traits and substance abuse. (1, 5, 7, 8)

2. Verbalize the relationship between being raised in an addictive family and the repeating the pattern of substance abuse. (1, 3, 4, 6)

3. Verbalize the rules of "don't talk, don't trust, don't feel" that were taught to him/her as a child and explain how these rules have made interpersonal relationships more difficult. (2, 4, 7, 9)

4. Verbalize an understanding of how ACOA traits contribute to substance abuse. (3, 4, 6)

5. Identify how the tendency to take on the parental role in interpersonal relationships is related to maintaining a feeling of security and control. (4, 5, 8)

6. Discuss the fears of abandonment experienced in the alcoholic home. (5, 7, 8)

7. Share the feeling of worthlessness that was learned in the alcoholic home and directly relate this feeling to his/her abuse of substances as a coping mechanism. (4, 6, 7, 8)

THERAPEUTIC INTERVENTIONS

1. Probe the feelings of powerlessness the patient experienced as a child in the alcoholic home and explore similarities to the patient's feelings when abusing chemicals.

   RP:* _____

   _____

2. Educate the patient about the ACOA rules of "don't talk, don't trust, don't feel," and explain how these rules make healthy relationships impossible.

   RP: _____

   _____

3. Teach the patient the effects that modeling, fear, and shame have on choosing a lifestyle of substance abuse.

   RP: _____

   _____

4. Explore how the dysfunctional family rules lead to uncomfortable feelings and escape into substance abuse.

   RP: _____

   _____

*RP = Responsible Professional

8. Identify the pattern in the alcoholic family of being ignored or punished when honest feelings were shared. (2, 4, 9, 12)

9. List the qualities and behaviors that should be evident in others before interpersonal trust can be built. (10, 11, 12, 24)

10. Increase the frequency of telling the truth rather than saying only what the patient thinks the other person wants to hear. Record each incident and feelings in a daily journal. (9, 12, 13)

11. Acknowledge the resistance to sharing personal problems; then share at least one problem in each therapy session. (2, 9, 10, 11)

12. Verbalize an understanding of how ACOA traits contribute to choosing partners and friends that have problems and need help. (5, 6, 14)

13. Initiate the encouragement of others in recovery to help reestablish a feeling of self-worth. (15, 16, 18, 19)

14. List ten reasons regular attendance at recovery group meetings is necessary to arrest ACOA traits and addiction. (15, 16, 19, 20, 21)

15. Discuss fears related to attendance at recovery

5. Assist the patient in understanding how early childhood experiences lead to fears of abandonment, rejection, neglect, and assumption of the caretaker role that is detrimental to intimate relationships.
   RP: _____
   _____

6. Discuss the relationship between ACOA traits and substance abuse.
   RP: _____
   _____

7. Probe the patient's fears of violence, abandonment, unpredictability, and embarrassment when the parent was abusing chemicals.
   RP: _____
   _____

8. Teach the patient that low self-esteem results from being raised in an alcoholic home, where emotional rejection, broken promises, abuse, neglect, poverty, and lost social status are common.
   RP: _____
   _____

9. Probe how the patient's family responded to expressions of feelings, wishes, and wants and why it became dangerous for the

group meetings and develop specific, written plans to deal with each fear. (4, 5, 17)

16. Verbalize how a recovery group can become the healthy family the patient never had. (15, 16, 19)

17. List five ways that belief in and interaction with a higher power can reduce fears and aid in recovery. (16, 20, 21)

18. Verbalize a feeling of serenity that results from turning problems that are out of his/her control over to the higher power. (20, 21)

19. Practice assertiveness skills and keep a daily journal of the times the skills were used in interpersonal conflict. (22, 23)

20. Three times a day, begin a sentence to a friend with the words, "I feel . . ." and record it. (22, 23, 24)

21. To practice intimacy skills, share the personal experiences of each day (feelings, thoughts, behaviors) with one person that day. (22, 24)

__. _____
    _____

__. _____
    _____

__. _____
    _____

client to share feelings with others.

RP: _____

_____

10. Help the patient identify a set of character traits in others (honesty, sensitivity, kindness, etc.) that qualify them as trustworthy.

RP: _____

_____

11. Educate the patient about healthy interpersonal relationships based on openness, respect, and honesty, and explain the necessity of sharing feelings to build trust and mutual understanding.

RP: _____

_____

12. Teach the patient that the behavior of telling other people what we think they want to hear rather than the truth is based on fear of rejection learned in the alcoholic home. Then use modeling, role playing, and behavioral rehearsal to teach the client more honest communication skills.

RP: _____

_____

13. Teach problem-solving skills (i.e., identify the problem, brainstorm alternate solutions, examine the

advantages and disadvantages of each option, select an option, implement a course of action, and evaluate the result), and role-play sharing a problem with someone who might be of assistance.

RP: _____

_____

14. Help the patient understand that the strong need to help others is based on low self-esteem and need for acceptance learned in the alcoholic family of origin. Relate this caretaking behavior to choosing friends and partners that are chemically dependent or psychologically disturbed.

RP: _____

_____

15. Teach the patient that active involvement in a recovery group can aid in building trust in others and confidence in self.

RP: _____

_____

16. Help the patient develop an aftercare plan centered around regular attendance at AA/NA meetings.

RP: _____

_____

17. Probe the relationship
    between ACOA traits and
    fears of attending recovery
    group meetings.

    RP: _____

    _____

18. Discuss how the home
    group of AA/NA can func-
    tion as the healthy home
    the patient never had. Then
    help the patient realize why
    he/she needs such a home to
    recover.

    RP: _____

    _____

19. Educate the patient about
    the family atmosphere in a
    home AA/NA recovery group
    and explain how helping
    others can aid in recovery
    and reestablish a feeling of
    worth.

    RP: _____

    _____

20. Teach the patient that faith
    in a higher power can aid in
    recovery and arrest ACOA
    traits and addiction.

    RP: _____

    _____

21. Assign the patient to read
    the Alcoholics Anonymous
    Big Book and process the
    material in an individual or
    group therapy session.

    RP: _____

    _____

22. Using modeling, behavior rehearsal, and role playing, teach the patient healthy assertive skills; then apply these skills to several current problem situations.

    RP: _____

    _____

23. Teach the patient the assertive formula of "I feel . . . When you . . . I would prefer it if. . . ." Then role-play several applications in the patient's life.

    RP: _____

    _____

24. Teach the patient the "share-check method" of building trust, in which the degree of shared information is related to a proven level of trustworthiness. Use behavioral rehearsal of several situations in which the patient shares feelings.

    RP: _____

    _____

___. _____

    _____

    RP: _____

    _____

___. _____

    _____

    RP: _____

    _____

—. _____
   _____
RP: _____
   _____

—. _____
   _____
RP: _____
   _____

DIAGNOSTIC SUGGESTIONS

Axis I: 311   Depressive Disorder NOS
              300.00   Anxiety Disorder NOS
              309.81   Posttraumatic Stress Disorder
              V61.20   Parent-Child Relational Problem

              _____   _____
              _____

Axis II: 301.82   Avoidant Personality Disorder
              301.6   Dependent Personality Disorder
              301.9   Personality Disorder NOS

              _____   _____
              _____   _____

ANGER

BEHAVIORAL DEFINITIONS

1. History of explosive, aggressive outbursts, particularly when intoxicated, that lead to assaultive acts or destruction of property.
2. Tendency to blame others rather than accept responsibility for his or her own problem behavior.
3. Angry overreaction to perceived disapproval, rejection, or criticism.
4. Passively withholds feelings, then explodes in a violent rage.
5. Abuses substances to cope with angry feelings and relinquishes responsibility for aggression.
6. Persistent pattern of challenging or disrespecting authority figures.
7. Body language of tense muscles (e.g., clenched fists or jaw, glaring looks, or refusal to make eye contact).
8. Views aggression as a means to achieve needed power and control.
9. Use of verbally abusive language.

__. _____

_____

__. _____

_____

__. _____

_____

LONG-TERM GOALS

1. Maintain a program of recovery free of substance abuse and violent behavior.
2. Decrease the frequency of angry thoughts, feelings, and behaviors.

3. Develop the ability to think positively in anger-producing situations.

4. Stop blaming others and begin to accept responsibility for own feelings, thoughts, and behaviors.

5. Learn and implement stress management skills to reduce the level of stress and the irritability that accompanies it.

6. Understand the relationship between angry feelings and the feelings of hurt and worthlessness experienced in the family of origin.

7. Learn the assertive skills necessary to reduce angry feelings and solve problems in a less aggressive and more constructive manner.

8. Learn and demonstrate strategies to meet the needs of self rather than depending upon others.

9. Replace thoughts that trigger anger with positive self-talk that induces serenity.

—. _____
   _____

—. _____
   _____

—. _____
   _____

SHORT-TERM OBJECTIVES

1. Keep a daily anger log, writing down each situation that produced angry feelings and the thoughts associated with the situation; then rate the level of anger on a scale from 1 to 100. (1)

2. Identify and verbalize the pain and hurt of past and current life that fuels anger. (2, 3, 9)

THERAPEUTIC INTERVENTIONS

1. Process the patient's anger log and help uncover the dysfunctional thoughts that trigger anger.

   RP:*_____

   _____

2. Assign patient to list experiences of life that have hurt and led to anger and resentment.

   RP: _____

   _____

_____

*RP = Responsible Professional

3. Verbalize an understanding of how anger has been reinforced as a coping mechanism for stress. (3, 9)

4. Reduce the frequency and severity of temper outbursts and other aggressive behaviors. (4, 5, 17)

5. Verbalize regret and remorse for harmful consequences of anger as well as steps necessary to forgive self and react more constructively. (4, 5, 8, 17)

6. Decrease the frequency of negative, self-defeating thinking and increase the frequency of positive, self-enhancing self-talk. (1, 5, 9, 10)

7. Increase the frequency of assertive behaviors while reducing the frequency of aggressive behaviors. (4, 7)

8. Verbalize an understanding of the relationship between the feelings of worthlessness and hurt experienced in the family of origin and the current feelings of anger. (2, 8, 9, 10)

9. Verbalize an understanding of the need for and the process of forgiving others to reduce anger. (8, 9, 13)

10. Report a termination of assuming to know the negative thoughts, intentions, and feelings of others and start asking others for more information. (9, 10)

3. Teach the patient how anger blocks the awareness of pain, discharges uncomfortable feelings, erases guilt, and places the blame for problems on others.

RP: _____

_____

4. Teach the patient the impulse-control skill of "stop, look, listen, think, and plan" before acting.

RP: _____

_____

5. Use modeling and role reversal to make patient more aware of the negative consequences his/her aggressive behavior has had on others who have been the target of (e.g., spouse) or witness to (e.g., children) violence.

RP: _____

_____

6. Help the patient develop a list of positive, self-enhancing statements to use daily in building a positive and accurate self-image. Use role play and modeling to demonstrate implementation of positive self-talk.

RP: _____

_____

7. Teach assertiveness and its benefits through the use of

11. Verbalize an understanding of how angry thoughts and feelings can lead to increased risk of substance abuse. List instances in which anger has resulted in substance abuse. (11, 12)

12. List five reasons angry thoughts, feelings, and behaviors increase the risk of relapse. (11, 12, 14)

13. Make a list of the thoughts that trigger angry feelings and replace each thought with a more positive and accurate thought that is supportive to self and recovery. (6, 10, 13, 16)

14. Practice relaxation skills twice a day for 10 to 20 minutes. (15, 21)

15. Report instances of implementing stress management skills such as prayer to higher power, relaxation, sharing feelings, regular exercise, and healthy self-talk. (13, 15, 16, 17, 21)

16. Implement proactive steps to meet the needs of self without expecting other people to meet those needs and angrily blaming them when they fail to do so. (7, 18)

17. Report implementation of stopping the impulsive angry reaction (opening the hands, relaxing the muscles, using reassuring self-talk and a soft voice) when feelings of anger arise. (19)

role play and modeling, assignment of appropriate reading material (e.g., Alberti and Emmons, *Your Perfect Right*), or participation in an assertiveness training group.

RP: _____

_____

8. Assist patient in identifying who he/she needs to forgive and explain the long-term process involved in forgiveness versus a single magical event. Recommend reading Smedes (1991), *Forgive and Forget.*

RP: _____

_____

9. Probe the abuse and neglect in the family of origin and help the patient see how these feelings lead to a tendency to see people and situations as dangerous and threatening.

RP: _____

_____

10. Teach the patient about the tendency to read malicious intent into the words and actions of others; then use modeling, role playing, and behavioral rehearsal to show the patient how to ask other people what they think and feel.

RP: _____

_____

18. Practice the time-out technique five times with the therapist and significant other. Keep a record of using the technique in daily interactions. (19, 20, 21)

19. Develop an aftercare program that details what he/ she is going to do when feeling angry. (14, 15, 16, 17)

—. _____
   _____
—. _____
   _____
—. _____
   _____

11. Educate the patient about the tendency to abuse substances as a means of relieving uncomfortable feelings. Develop a list of several instances of occurrence.

   RP: _____

   _____

12. Teach the patient about the high-risk situations of strong negative emotions, social pressure, interpersonal conflict, strong positive emotions, and testing personal control. Discuss how anger, as strong negative emotion, places the patient at high risk for substance abuse.

   RP: _____

   _____

13. Teach the patient how to turn over perpetrators of pain to his/her higher power for judgment and punishment.

   RP: _____

   _____

14. Help the patient understand that thoughts of abandonment and rejection trigger feelings of worthlessness, hurt, and then anger.

   RP: _____

   _____

15. Teach the patient progressive relaxation skills and encourage their use twice a day for 10 to 20 minutes.

RP: _____

_____

16. Teach the patient the stress management skills of regular exercise and positive self-talk and explain their benefits.

RP: _____

_____

17. Teach the patient the importance of actively attending AA/NA meetings, getting a sponsor, reinforcing people around him/her, sharing feelings, and developing pleasurable leisure activities.

RP: _____

_____

18. Assist patient to develop a list of his/her own needs and wishes and to establish the personal actions necessary to attain these rather than being angry with others for not meeting his/her needs and wishes.

RP: _____

_____

19. Using modeling, role playing, and behavioral rehearsal, show the patient how to stop the impulse to react with anger (e.g., relax

the muscles; use positive,
comforting self-talk; speak
softly in frustrating, threatening, or hurtful situa-
tions).

RP: _____

_____

20. Develop a time-out contract
    between the patient and
    his/her significant other.
    Role-play the technique
    using five different situa-
    tions.

    RP: _____

    _____

21. Help the patient develop a
    list of adaptive actions
    he/she is going to take to
    deflect feelings of anger
    (e.g., calling a sponsor,
    being assertive but not
    aggressive, taking a time-
    out, praying to higher
    power) to avoid relapse.

    RP: _____

    _____

__. _____

    _____

    RP: _____

    _____

__. _____

    _____

    RP: _____

    _____

—.   _____

   _____

RP: _____

   _____

DIAGNOSTIC SUGGESTIONS

Axis I:

312.8	Conduct Disorder
313.81	Oppositional Defiant Disorder
296.xx	Bipolar I Disorder
296.89	Bipolar II Disorder
312.34	Intermittent Explosive Disorder
312.30	Impulse-Control Disorder NOS
309.4	Adjustment Disorder With Mixed Disturbance of Emotions and Conduct
V71.01	Adult Antisocial Behavior
V71.02	Child or Adolescent Antisocial Behavior
_____	_____

Axis II:

301.0	Paranoid Personality Disorder
301.7	Antisocial Personality Disorder
301.83	Borderline Personality Disorder
301.9	Personality Disorder NOS
301.81	Narcissistic Personality Disorder
_____	_____
_____	_____

ANTISOCIAL BEHAVIOR

BEHAVIORAL DESCRIPTIONS

1. A history of breaking the rules or the law (often under the influence of drugs or alcohol) to get his or her own way.
2. A pervasive pattern of disregard for and violation of the rights of others.
3. Consistently blames other people for his or her own problems and behaviors.
4. Uses aggressive behavior to manipulate, intimidate, or control others.
5. Chronic pattern of dishonesty.
6. Hedonistic, self-centered lifestyle with little regard for the needs and welfare of others.
7. Lack of empathy for the feelings of others, even if they are friends or family.
8. A pattern of criminal activity and substance abuse going back into the adolescent years.
9. Engages in dangerous, thrill-seeking behavior without regard for the safety of self or others.
10. Impulsively makes decisions without giving thought to the consequences for others.
11. Failure to keep commitments, promises, or obligations toward others, including his or her children, family, or significant others.
12. A history of many broken relationships with a lack of loyalty shown in intimate as well as superficial relationships.

—. _____
   _____

—. _____
   _____

—. _____
  _____

LONG-TERM GOALS

1. Develop a program of recovery that is free from substance abuse and the negative influences of antisocial behavior.
2. Learn the importance of helping others in recovery.
3. Learn how antisocial behavior and substance abuse is self-defeating.
4. Understand criminal thinking and develop self-talk that respects the welfare and rights of others.
5. Stop committing crimes and understand why illegal activity is harmful to self and others.
6. Understand the importance of a program of recovery that demands rigorous honesty.
7. Develop a structured program of recovery that includes regular attendance at recovery group meetings.
8. Obey the law as an essential part of a program of recovery.
9. Learn and practice behaviors that are prosocial.
10. Develop a program of recovery that demands rigorous honesty.
11. Respect the rights and feelings of others.
12. Take responsibility for his or her own behavior.
13. Demonstrate honesty, reliability, and commitment in relationships.
14. Abstain from drugs and alcohol as necessary part of controlling and changing antisocial impulses and behavior.

—. _____
  _____
—. _____
  _____
—. _____
  _____

SHORT-TERM OBJECTIVES

1. Verbalize an acceptance of powerlessness and unmanageability over antisocial behavior and substance abuse. (1, 2, 3)

2. Verbalize how substance abuse fosters antisocial behavior and how antisocial behavior encourages substance abuse. (2, 3)

3. State how antisocial behavior and substance abuse are associated with irrational thinking (AA's concept of "insanity"). (3)

4. Consistently follow all rules. (4, 5)

5. Identify and verbalize the consequences that failure to comply with the rules/limits has had on self and others. (4, 5, 6, 7)

6. List five occasions on which antisocial behaviors led to negative consequences, and list the many decisions that were made along the way. (4, 5, 6, 7)

7. List the ways in which dishonesty is self-defeating. (8, 9)

8. List the reasons criminal activity leads to a negative self-image. (9)

THERAPEUTIC INTERVENTIONS

1. Help the patient understand the self-defeating nature of antisocial behavior and substance abuse.

   RP:* _____

   _____

2. Help the patient see the relationship between antisocial behavior and substance abuse.

   RP: _____

   _____

3. Help the patient understand that doing the same things over and over but expecting different results is irrational, or what AA calls "insane."

   RP: _____

   _____

4. Assign appropriate consequences when the patient fails to follow rules or expectations.

   RP: _____

   _____

5. Show the patient several examples of rule/limit breaking leading to negative consequences to self and others.

   RP: _____

   _____

_____

*RP = Responsible Professional

9. Verbalize how criminal thinking (e.g., a feeling of entitlement, needing power, lack of empathy, superoptimism, discounting others) is used to avoid responsibility and to blame others. (10)

10. Verbalize an understanding of why blaming others prevents learning from mistakes of the past. (11, 12)

11. Decrease frequency of statements blaming others or circumstances while increasing frequency of statements accepting responsibility for own behavior, thoughts, and feelings. (11, 12)

12. Identify historic and current sources for the pattern of rebellious actions. (12)

13. Develop a list of prosocial behaviors and practice one of these behaviors each day. (13, 14, 19)

14. Write a list of typical criminal thoughts; then replace each thought with a thought that is respectful to self and others. (14)

15. List five ways AA/NA meetings and a higher power can assist the patient in overcoming antisocial behavior and substance abuse. (15)

16. Receive feedback/redirection from staff/therapist without making negative gestures or remarks. (16)

6. Attempt to sensitize patient to his/her lack of empathy for others by revisiting consequences of behavior on others. Use role-reversal techniques.

RP: _____

_____

7. Teach the patient that many negative consequences are preceded by decisions based in criminal thinking.

RP: _____

_____

8. Assist the patient in understanding why dishonesty results in more lies, loss of trust from others, and ultimate rejection.

RP: _____

_____

9. Help the patient understand why criminal activity leads to feelings of low self-esteem.

RP: _____

_____

10. Teach the patient how criminal thinking (e.g., superoptimism, little empathy for others, power orientation, a sense of entitlement, self-centeredness) leads to antisocial behavior and substance abuse.

RP: _____

_____

17. Develop a written plan to address all pending legal problems in a constructive manner. (17)

18. Verbalize why it is essential in recovery from antisocial traits and substance abuse to give assistance to others, and give examples of how he/she has been supportive toward others. (18)

19. Encourage at least one person in recovery each day. (18, 19)

20. State the reasons that having the trust of others is important. (20)

21. Articulate antisocial and substance abuse behaviors that have resulted in others' pain and disappointment, and therefore in a loss of their trust. (21, 22)

22. Verbalize a desire to keep commitments to others and list ways that he/she could prove self to be responsible, reliable, loyal and faithful. (23)

23. Verbalize several ways a sponsor can be helpful in recovery; then make contact with a temporary sponsor. (24)

24. List the recovery groups and continuing therapy the patient plans to attend in aftercare. (25)

11. Help the patient understand how blaming others results in a failure to learn from mistakes, and thus the same mistakes recur.

RP: _____

_____

12. Explore with the patient the reasons for blaming others for own problems and behaviors and how he/she may have learned this behavior in a punishing family environment.

RP: _____

_____

13. Explain the difference between antisocial and prosocial behaviors; then help the patient develop a list of prosocial behaviors (e.g., helping others) to practice each day.

RP: _____

_____

14. Confront the patient's antisocial beliefs about the lack of respect for the rights and feelings of others, and model thoughtful attitudes and beliefs about the welfare of others.

RP: _____

_____

15. Discuss with the patient the various ways recovery groups and a higher

___. _____
   _____
___. _____
   _____
___. _____
   _____

power can assist him/her in recovery.

RP: _____

_____

16. Confront the patient when he/she breaks the rules, blames others, or makes excuses.

RP: _____

_____

17. Assist the patient in addressing each legal problem honestly, taking responsibility for his/her behavior.

RP: _____

_____

18. Teach the patient why it is essential to attend recovery groups and help others.

RP: _____

_____

19. Using modeling, role playing, and behavioral rehearsal, practice with the patient how he/she can encourage others in recovery.

RP: _____

_____

20. Assist patient in developing a list of reasons that the trust of others is important as a basis for any human relationship.

RP: _____

_____

21. Encourage patient to be honest in acknowledging how he/she has hurt others.

    RP: _____

    _____

22. Confront any denial of responsibility for irresponsible, self-centered, and impulsive behaviors.

    RP: _____

    _____

23. Discuss the importance of keeping commitments and promises to others and ways to prove self as trustworthy in relationships.

    RP: _____

    _____

24. Introduce the patient to his/her AA/NA sponsor or encourage him/her to ask a stable recovery person to be a sponsor; teach patient the many ways a sponsor can be used in recovery.

    RP: _____

    _____

25. Help the patient develop an aftercare program that specifically outlines which AA meetings will be attended and which psychotherapist he/she will be working with.

    RP: _____

    _____

—. _____

_____

RP: _____

_____

—. _____

_____

RP: _____

_____

—. _____

_____

RP: _____

_____

DIAGNOSTIC SUGGESTIONS

Axis I:	312.8	Conduct Disorder
	313.81	Oppositional Defiant Disorder
	309.3	Adjustment Disorder With Disturbance of Conduct
	312.34	Intermittent Explosive Disorder
	V71.01	Adult Antisocial Behavior
	V71.02	Child or Adolescent Antisocial Behavior
	_____	_____
	_____	
Axis II:	301.7	Antisocial Personality Disorder
	301.83	Borderline Personality Disorder
	301.81	Narcissistic Personality Disorder
	_____	_____
	_____	_____

ANXIETY

BEHAVIORAL DEFINITIONS

1. Excessive fear and worry about several life circumstances that have no factual or logical basis.
2. Constant worry about family, job, social interactions, or health.
3. Tendency to blame self for the slightest imperfection or mistake.
4. Fear of saying or doing something foolish in a social situation due to lack of confidence in social skills.
5. Symptoms of autonomic hyperactivity such as cardiac palpitations, shortness of breath, sweaty palms, dry mouth, trouble swallowing, nausea, or diarrhea.
6. Symptoms of motor tension such as restlessness, tiredness, shakiness, or muscle tension.
7. Abuse of substances in an attempt to control anxiety symptoms.
8. Symptoms of hypervigilance such as feeling constantly on edge, difficulty concentrating, sleep problems, irritability.

—. _____
_____
_____
—. _____
_____
—. _____
_____

LONG-TERM GOALS

1. Maintain a program of recovery free from substance abuse and excessive anxiety.
2. End substance abuse as a means of escaping anxiety and practice constructive coping behaviors.

3. Decrease anxious thoughts and increase positive self-enhancing self-talk.
4. Reduce overall stress levels, reducing excessive worry and muscle tension.
5. Learn to relax and think accurately and logically about events.
6. Learn the relationship between anxiety and substance abuse.
7. Develop the social skills necessary to reduce excessive anxiety in social situations and terminate reliance on substance abuse as a coping mechanism.
8. Resolve the conflict that is at the source of anxiety.

—. _____
_____
_____
—. _____
_____
_____
—. _____
_____

SHORT-TERM OBJECTIVES

1. Keep a daily journal of anxiety episodes, including the situation that caused anxious feelings and the negative thoughts that fueled anxiety. Then rank each anxiety-producing situation on a scale from 1 to 100. (1, 6)

2. Acknowledge the powerlessness and unmanageability caused by excessive anxiety and substance abuse. (2, 3, 4)

3. List reasons anxiety led to more substance abuse and substance abuse led to more anxiety. (2, 3)

THERAPEUTIC INTERVENTIONS

1. Assign the patient to keep a daily record of anxiety, including each situation that caused anxious feelings. Process the journal material and help the patient uncover the negative thoughts that fueled the anxiety.

   RP:*_____

   _____

2. Help the patient see how anxiety and powerlessness over substance abuse has made his/her life unmanageable.

   RP: _____

   _____

---
*RP = Responsible Professional

4. Verbalize the irrationality (AA's insanity) of excessive anxiety and substance abuse. (3, 4, 5)

5. Explain how and why irrational thoughts form the basis for anxiety. (5, 6)

6. List specific worries, and use logic and reasoning to replace irrational thoughts with rational thinking. (5, 6)

7. Implement positive self-talk to reduce or eliminate the anxiety. (6, 7, 8, 9, 10)

8. List ten positive self-enhancing statements that he/she will read several times a day, particularly when feeling anxious. (7, 8, 9, 10)

9. Comply with a physician evaluation to determine if psychopharmacological intervention is warranted; then take any medications as directed. (11, 12)

10. List several ways a higher power can assist in a program of recovery from anxiety and substance abuse. (13, 14)

11. Report on the instances that the patient has released worries and anxieties to a higher power of his/her own understanding. (13, 14)

3. Teach the patient about the relationship between anxiety and substance abuse—that is, how the substance was used to treat the anxious symptoms and why more substance use became necessary.

RP: _____

_____

4. Explain the AA concept of insanity and help the patient understand that anxiety and substance abuse are "insane."

RP: _____

_____

5. Help the patient understand the irrational nature of the underlying thoughts that are producing his/her fears.

RP: _____

_____

6. Help the patient identify specific worries; then facilitate the patient's use of logic and reasoning to challenge the irrational thoughts associated with the fear and to replace those thoughts with rational ones.

RP: _____

_____

12. Identify the fears that were learned in the family of origin and relate these fears to current anxiety levels. (15, 16, 17)

13. Write a specific plan to follow when anxious and craving substance use. (8, 14, 18)

14. Develop a leisure program that will increase pleasurable activities and affirm self. (19)

15. Practice relaxation techniques twice a day for 10 to 20 minutes. (20)

16. Exercise at least three times a week at a training heart rate (220 – age × .75 to .85) for at least 20 minutes. (21)

17. Write an autobiography detailing those behaviors in the past that are related to current anxiety or guilt and the use of substance abuse as a means of escape. (15, 16, 22)

18. Increase assertive behaviors to deal more effectively and directly with stress, conflict, and responsibilities. (23, 24)

19. Increase the frequency of speaking up with confidence in social situations. (23, 24)

20. Develop a program of recovery that includes helping others at regular recovery group meetings. (25)

7. Help the patient develop reality-based cognitive messages that will increase self-confidence in coping with fears and anxieties.

   RP: _____

   _____

8. Assist the patient in developing a list of ten positive statements to read to him-/herself several times a day, particularly when feeling anxious.

   RP: _____

   _____

9. Assign patient to read *What to Say When You Talk to Yourself* (Helmstetter) and process key ideas with therapist.

   RP: _____

   _____

10. Reinforce use of more realistic, positive messages to self in interpreting life events.

    RP: _____

    _____

11. Physician will determine if psychopharmacological intervention is warranted, order medication, titrate medication, and monitor for side effects.

    RP: _____

    _____

___. _____

  _____

___. _____

  _____

___. _____

  _____

12. Staff will administer medi-
    cation as directed by the
    physician and monitor for
    side effects and effective-
    ness.

    RP: _____

    _____

13. Teach the patient the bene-
    fits of turning his/her will
    and life over to the care of a
    higher power of his/her own
    understanding.

    RP: _____

    _____

14. Using an AA step three
    exercise, show the patient
    how to turn over problems,
    worries, and anxieties to a
    higher power and trust that
    the higher power is going to
    help him/her resolve the sit-
    uation.

    RP: _____

    _____

15. Probe the patient's family-
    of-origin experiences for
    fear-producing situations
    and help the patient relate
    these past events to current
    thoughts, feelings, and
    behaviors.

    RP: _____

    _____

16. Encourage and support the
    patient in verbally express-
    ing and clarifying his/her
    feelings associated with

past rejection experiences, harsh criticism, abandonment, or trauma.

RP: _____

_____

17. Assign patient to read the books *Healing the Shame That Binds You* (Bradshaw) and *Facing Shame* (Fossum and Mason); process key concepts with therapist.

RP: _____

_____

18. Help the patient develop an alternative constructive plan of action (e.g., use relaxation exercises and physical exercise, call a sponsor, go to a meeting, call the counselor, talk to someone) when feeling anxious and craving substance use.

RP: _____

_____

19. Help the patient develop a plan of engaging in pleasurable leisure activities (e.g., clubs, hobbies, church, sporting activities, social activities, games) that will increase enjoyment of life and affirm self.

RP: _____

_____

20. Using relaxation techniques (e.g., progressive relaxation, guided imagery, biofeedback), teach the patient how to relax completely; then assign him/her to relax twice a day for 10 to 20 minutes.

    RP: _____

    _____

21. Using current physical fitness levels, increase the patient's exercise by 10 percent a week until he/she is exercising three times a week at a training heart rate (220 − age × .75 to .85) for at least 20 minutes.

    RP: _____

    _____

22. Using an AA step four exercise, have the patient write an autobiography detailing the exact nature of his/her wrongs; then teach the patient how to begin to forgive him-/herself and others.

    RP: _____

    _____

23. Teach assertiveness skills to help the patient communicate thoughts, feelings, and needs more openly and directly.

    RP: _____

    _____

24. Use role play and behavioral rehearsal to improve the patient's assertiveness and social skills.

    RP: _____

    _____

25. Help the patient develop a structured program of recovery that includes helping others at regular AA/NA recovery groups.

    RP: _____

    _____

__. _____

    _____

    RP: _____

    _____

__. _____

    _____

    RP: _____

    _____

__. _____

    _____

    RP: _____

    _____

DIAGNOSTIC SUGGESTIONS

Axis I:	309.21	Separation Anxiety Disorder
	291.8	Alcohol-Induced Anxiety Disorder
	292.89	Substance-Induced Anxiety Disorder
	296.90	Mood Disorder NOS
	300.01	Panic Disorder Without Agoraphobia
	300.21	Panic Disorder With Agoraphobia
	300.29	Specific Phobia
	300.23	Social Phobia
	300.3	Obsessive-Compulsive Disorder
	309.81	Posttraumatic Stress Disorder
	308.3	Acute Stress Disorder
	300.02	Generalized Anxiety Disorder
	309.24	Adjustment Disorder With Anxiety
	309.28	Adjustment Disorder With Mixed Anxiety and Depressed Mood
	_____	_____
	_____	_____
Axis II:	301.0	Paranoid Personality Disorder
	301.83	Borderline Personality Disorder
	301.50	Histrionic Personality Disorder
	301.82	Avoidant Personality Disorder
	301.6	Dependent Personality Disorder
	301.4	Obsessive-Compulsive Personality Disorder
	301.9	Personality Disorder NOS
	_____	_____
	_____	_____

ATTENTION-DEFICIT / HYPERACTIVITY DISORDER

BEHAVIORAL DESCRIPTIONS

1. A pattern of restlessness and hyperactivity leading to attention deficit or learning disability.
2. Unable to focus attention long enough to learn appropriately.
3. Often fidgets with hands or squirms in seat.
4. Often leaves seat in situations where sitting is required.
5. Moves about excessively in situations in which it is inappropriate.
6. Unable to exclude extraneous stimulation.
7. Blurts out answers before the questions have been completed.
8. Has difficulty waiting in lines or waiting his or her turn.
9. Often intrudes or talks excessively.
10. Acts too quickly on feelings without thought or deliberation.
11. Low self-esteem and poor social skills that lead to alienation from peers.

___. _____
    _____
___. _____
    _____
___. _____
    _____

LONG-TERM GOALS

1. Maintain a program of recovery from substance abuse and reduce the negative effects of Attention-Deficit/Hyperactivity Disorder (ADHD) on learning, social interaction, and self-esteem.
2. Develop the coping skills necessary to improve ADHD and eliminate substance abuse.

3. Understand the relationship between ADHD symptoms and substance abuse.
4. Develop the skills necessary to bring ADHD symptoms under control so normal learning can take place.
5. Create an environment relatively free of extraneous stimulation so that the patient can concentrate.
6. Decrease impulsivity by learning how to stop, think, and plan before acting.

—. _____

_____

_____

—. _____

_____

_____

—. _____

_____

SHORT-TERM OBJECTIVES

1. Complete psychological testing to confirm the diagnosis of ADHD. (1, 2, 3)

2. Complete psychological testing to rule out emotional factors or learning disabilities as the basis for maladaptive behavior. (1, 2, 3)

3. Monitor symptoms of ADHD on a daily basis and rate the severity of symptoms each day on a scale of 1 to 100. (4)

4. Verbalize the powerlessness and unmanageability that resulted from treating ADHD symptoms with substance abuse. (5, 6)

THERAPEUTIC INTERVENTIONS

1. Arrange for thorough psychological testing to confirm the presence of ADHD in the patient.

   RP:*_____

   _____

2. Arrange for psychological testing to rule out emotional factors or learning disabilities as the basis for the patient's maladaptive behavior.

   RP: _____

   _____

_____

*RP = Responsible Professional

5. Verbalize the relationship between ADHD and substance abuse. (5, 6)

6. Implement a program of recovery structured to bring ADHD and substance abuse under control. (7, 8, 9)

7. List five ways a higher power can be used to assist in recovery from ADHD and substance abuse. (8)

8. Comply with a physician evaluation to determine if a psychotropic intervention is warranted and take any medications as directed. (9, 10)

9. Implement remedial procedures for any learning disabilities that add to frustration. (11)

10. Reduce environmental stimulation to the point that the patient can concentrate and new learning can take place. (12, 14)

11. Keep lists and use a calendar to remember daily appointments and obligations. (13)

12. Practice taking time-outs and breaks when feeling restless or irritable. (14, 15)

13. Practice extending concentration in gradual increments, and self-reinforce each extension. (14, 15)

14. Verbalize an understanding of the importance of learning in small increments of

3. Give feedback to the patient and his/her family regarding psychological testing results.

RP: _____

_____

4. Teach the patient how to monitor ADHD symptoms and rate the severity of symptoms on a scale of 1 to 100 each day.

RP: _____

_____

5. Using a step one exercise, help the patient accept his/her powerlessness over and inability to manage ADHD symptoms and substance abuse.

RP: _____

_____

6. Using a biopsychosocial approach, explain the relationship between ADHD symptoms and the use of substances to control symptoms.

RP: _____

_____

7. Help the patient develop a program of recovery that includes the elements necessary to bring ADHD and substance abuse under control (e.g., medication, behavior modification, environmental controls,

time and taking breaks as needed to keep ADHD symptoms under control. (15, 16)

15. Reduce impulsive behavior and demonstrate the ability to stop, think, and plan before acting. (17, 18)

16. Verbalize the feelings of shame and frustration that accompany failure to learn because of ADHD. (19)

17. List the negative messages given to self in a learning situation and replace each with an encouraging, affirming message. (19, 20)

18. Identify specific instances when the negative emotions associated with failure to learn were a trigger for substance abuse, and verbalize constructive coping mechanisms to use in future learning situations. (19, 20, 21)

19. Increase the frequency of positive interaction with peers (e.g., use calm tones, respectfully time verbal contributions, consider the impact of comments, use appropriate humility). (22, 23)

20. Verbalize satisfaction with self and others regarding "fitting in" socially. (23, 24)

21. Practice relaxation techniques two times a day for 10 to 20 minutes. (25, 26)

aftercare meetings, further therapy).
RP: _____

_____

8. Explain the AA concept of a higher power and discuss how this power can assist the patient in recovery.
RP: _____

_____

9. Physician will order psychotropic medications as warranted, titrate medications and monitor for side effects.
RP: _____

_____

10. Staff will administer medications as ordered by the physician and monitor for side effects.
RP: _____

_____

11. Have an educational specialist design remedial procedures for any learning disabilities that may be present in addition to ADHD.
RP: _____

_____

12. Help the patient create an environment relatively free of extraneous stimulation so that learning can take place.
RP: _____

_____

22. Report instances when relaxation techniques reduced tension and frustration while increasing focus in a learning situation. (25, 26)

23. Develop and implement an exercise program that includes exercise at a training heart rate (220 − age × .75 to .85) for at least 20 minutes at least three times a week. (27)

24. Develop an aftercare program that includes regularly attending recovery group meetings, getting a sponsor, and continuing the therapy necessary to bring ADHD and substance abuse under control. (7, 28)

__. _____
    _____

__. _____
    _____

__. _____
    _____

13. Teach the patient how to make lists and keep a calendar to remind him/her about appointments and daily obligations.

    RP: _____

    _____

14. Using modeling, role playing, and behavioral rehearsal, show the patient how to take time-outs and breaks when feeling restless or irritable.

    RP: _____

    _____

15. Explain how to extend periods of concentration in small increments; then teach the patient how to reinforce him-/herself each time.

    RP: _____

    _____

16. Assist the patient in setting up learning periods in small increments of time, taking breaks as needed to keep ADHD symptoms under control.

    RP: _____

    _____

17. Using modeling, role playing, and behavioral rehearsal, show the patient how to stop, think, and plan before acting. Then practice this technique several times.

    RP: _____

    _____

18. Teach the patient techniques to use (e.g., relax, exercise, talk to someone, take a time-out) when feeling restless or irritable.

   RP: _____

   _____

19. Explore negative emotions associated with failure to learn.

   RP: _____

   _____

20. Train patient to replace negative expectations and disparaging self-talk with positive self-talk in a learning situation.

   RP: _____

   _____

21. Review specific instances of failure to learn and the negative emotions associated with the experience. Role-play and model constructive alternative coping behaviors (e.g., focus cognitively, breathe deeply, make lists, reduce distractions, shorten learning sessions, repeat instructions verbally).

   RP: _____

   _____

22. Using role playing, modeling, and behavior rehearsal, teach social skills that control impulsivity, reduce

alienation, and build self-esteem.

RP: _____

_____

23. Direct group therapy sessions that focus on social skill enhancement, getting feedback from peers for patient's socialization behavior.

RP: _____

_____

24. Reinforce positive social interaction with peers and explore the positive self-esteem that results from the successful interactions.

RP: _____

_____

25. Using techniques like progressive relaxation or biofeedback, teach the patient how to relax completely; then assign the patient to relax twice a day for 10 to 20 minutes.

RP: _____

_____

26. As a coping and focusing mechanism, encourage patient to implement relaxation skills when feeling tense and frustrated by a learning situation.

RP: _____

_____

27. Using current fitness levels, help the patient develop an exercise program; then increase the exercise by 10 percent each week until the patient is exercising at a training heart rate (220 − age × .75 to .85) for at least 20 minutes at least three times a week.

    RP: _____

    _____

28. Help the patient develop an aftercare program that includes regularly attending recovery group meetings, getting a sponsor, and continuing the therapy necessary to bring ADHD and substance abuse under control.

    RP: _____

    _____

__. _____

    _____

    RP: _____

    _____

__. _____

    _____

    RP: _____

    _____

__. _____

    _____

    RP: _____

    _____

DIAGNOSTIC SUGGESTIONS

Axis I:	315.9	Learning Disorder NOS
	314.01	Attention-Deficit/Hyperactivity Disorder, Combined Type
	314.01	Attention-Deficit/Hyperactivity Disorder, Predominantly Hyperactive-Impulsive Type
	314.9	Attention-Deficit/Hyperactivity Disorder NOS
	312.8	Conduct Disorder
	313.81	Oppositional Defiant Disorder
	312.9	Disruptive Behavior Disorder NOS
	291.8	Alcohol-Induced Mood Disorder
	292.xx	Substance-Induced Mood Disorder
	309.4	Adjustment Disorder With Mixed Disturbance of Emotions and Conduct
	312.30	Impulse-Control Disorder NOS
	_____	_____
	_____	_____
Axis II:	301.7	Antisocial Personality Disorder
	301.83	Borderline Personality Disorder
	_____	_____
	_____	_____

ATTENTION-DEFICIT/ INATTENTIVE DISORDER

BEHAVIORAL DESCRIPTIONS

1. Inability to sustain attention long enough to learn normally at work or school.
2. Fails to give sufficient attention to details and tends to make careless mistakes.
3. Has difficulty sustaining attention at work, school, or play.
4. Often does not seem to listen when spoken to directly.
5. Often does not follow through on instructions and fails to finish tasks.
6. Has difficulty organizing events, material, or time.
7. Avoids tasks and activities that require concentration.
8. Too easily distracted by extraneous stimulation.
9. Often forgets daily obligations.

___. _____

_____

___. _____

_____

___. _____

_____

LONG-TERM GOALS

1. Maintain a program of recovery free from substance abuse and the negative effects of attention-deficit disorder.
2. Demonstrate sustained attention and concentration for consistently longer periods of time.
3. Understand the negative influence of attention-deficit disorder on substance use.

4. Structure a recovery program sufficient to maintain abstinence and reduce the negative effects of attention-deficit disorder on learning and self-esteem.
5. Learn relaxation and exercise skills to cope with restlessness and irritability.
6. Develop positive self-talk when faced with problems caused by attention-deficit disorder or substance abuse.

—. _____

_____

—. _____

_____

—. _____

_____

SHORT-TERM OBJECTIVES

1. Complete psychological testing to confirm the diagnosis of ADHD. (1, 2, 3)

2. Complete psychological testing to rule out emotional factors or learning disabilities as the basis for maladaptive behavior. (1, 2, 3)

3. Verbalize several reasons attention-deficit symptoms lead to substance abuse. (4, 5)

4. List the ways in which using substance abuse to cope with symptoms of attention-deficit disorder and the feelings that result from it leads to powerlessness and unmanageability. (5, 7)

THERAPEUTIC INTERVENTIONS

1. Arrange for thorough psychological testing to confirm the presence of ADHD in the patient.
   RP:*_____

   _____

2. Arrange for psychological testing to rule out emotional factors or learning disabilities as the basis for the patient's maladaptive behavior.
   RP: _____

   _____

3. Give feedback to the patient and his/her family regarding psychological testing results.
   RP: _____

   _____

_____

*RP = Responsible Professional

5. Verbalize ten reasons attention deficit disorder leads to substance abuse. (4, 6, 8)

6. Verbalize the interpersonal difficulties caused by or exacerbated by symptoms of attention-deficit disorder and substance use. (6, 7)

7. Verbalize an understanding of the etiology of attention-deficit disorder and substance abuse. (4, 8)

8. Identify the feelings of shame and frustration experienced when dealing with a failure to learn due to attention-deficit disorder and state how chemicals were used to control uncomfortable feelings. (6, 9)

9. List the negative messages given to self in a learning situation and replace each with an encouraging, affirming message. (10, 11)

10. Identify specific instances when the negative emotions associated with failure to learn were a trigger for substance abuse; verbalize constructive coping mechanisms to use in future learning situations. (10, 11)

11. List ways in which a program of recovery can help eliminate the negative effects of attention-deficit disorder and substance abuse. (12, 16, 18)

12. Comply with a physician evaluation to determine if psychopharmacological

4. Help the patient understand the reasons why attention-deficit disorder leads to substance abuse to control symptoms.

RP: _____

_____

5. Using an AA step one exercise, help the patient to correlate attention-deficit disorder and substance abuse with powerlessness and unmanageability.

RP: _____

_____

6. Explain how the ADD symptoms of learning difficulties, impulsivity, and social alienation can make the patient vulnerable to substance abuse.

RP: _____

_____

7. Probe the relationship problems caused by or exacerbated by attention-deficit disorder and substance abuse.

RP: _____

_____

8. Teach the patient about the biopsychosocial events that cause attention-deficit disorder and substance abuse.

RP: _____

_____

intervention is warranted; then take medications as directed. (13, 14)

13. Implement remedial procedures for learning disabilities that add to frustration. (15)

14. List five ways a higher power can assist in dealing with the symptoms of attention-deficit disorder and substance abuse. (12, 16)

15. Keep lists of all scheduled activities and obligations and mark off each item as completed. (17)

16. List techniques that can be used to reduce the negative effects of attention-deficit disorder. (18, 19, 20, 21)

17. Create and utilize a learning environment that is relatively free of extraneous stimulation so that productive learning can take place. (19)

18. Develop and demonstrate the coping skills to use when experiencing attention-deficit disorder symptoms or craving substance abuse. (20, 21, 22, 24)

19. Practice relaxation techniques twice a day for at least 10 to 20 minutes. (21)

20. Report instances when relaxation technique reduced tension and frustration and increased focus in a learning situation. (22)

9. Probe the feelings the patient had when trying to deal with the failure to learn due to symptoms of attention-deficit disorder and discuss how chemical abuse was used to avoid uncomfortable feelings.

RP: _____

_____

10. Train patient to replace negative expectations and disparaging self-talk with positive self-talk in a learning situation.

RP: _____

_____

11. Review specific instances of failure to learn and the negative emotions associated with the experience. Role-play and model constructive alternative coping behaviors (e.g., focus cognitively, breathe deeply, make lists, reduce distractions, shorten learning sessions, repeat instructions verbally).

RP: _____

_____

12. Help the patient see how working on a program of recovery can aid in reducing the negative influence of attention-deficit disorder and substance abuse.

RP: _____

_____

21. Family members verbalize what each person can do to assist the patient in recovery. (23)

22. Exercise at a training heart rate (220 – age × .75 to .85) at least three times a week for at least 20 minutes. Use exercise as a coping mechanism when tense. (24)

__. _____
    _____

__. _____
    _____

__. _____
    _____

13. Physician will examine the patient to determine if psychopharmacological intervention is warranted, order medications as indicated, titrate medications, and observe for side effects.

    RP: _____

    _____

14. Staff will administer medications as ordered by the physician and monitor for side effects and effectiveness.

    RP: _____

    _____

15. Design remedial procedures for any learning disabilities that may be present in addition to attention-deficit disorder.

    RP: _____

    _____

16. Help the patient understand the AA concept of a higher power and explain ways a higher power can assist the patient in recovery.

    RP: _____

    _____

17. Assist the patient in developing calendars and lists detailing activities and obligations.

    RP: _____

    _____

18. Help the patient develop a list of the things he/she can do to reduce the negative effects of attention-deficit disorder (e.g., reduce extraneous stimulation, make lists and reminders, take medication, use relaxation techniques, talk to someone, go to AA/NA meetings, engage in physical exercise).

    RP: _____

    _____

19. Help the patient develop a quiet place free of extraneous stimulation where he/she can concentrate and learn.

    RP: _____

    _____

20. Teach the patient about the relapse-prevention skills of going to meetings, talking to someone, calling a sponsor, using relaxation techniques, engaging in physical exercise, and turning worries over to a higher power.

    RP: _____

    _____

21. Using relaxation techniques such as progressive relaxation, guided imagery, and biofeedback, teach the patient how to relax; then assign him/her to relax twice a day for 10 to 20 minutes.

    RP: _____

    _____

22. Encourage patient to implement relaxation skills as a coping and focusing mechanism when feeling tense and frustrated by a learning situation.

    RP: _____

    _____

23. In a family session, teach the family members about attention-deficit disorder and substance abuse, going over what each family member can do to assist the patient in recovery (e.g., go to Alanon meetings, reinforce positive coping skills, be patient, keep expectations realistic, go to ADHD support group).

    RP: _____

    _____

24. Using current physical fitness levels, help the patient develop an exercise program; then increase exercise until the patient is exercising at a training heart rate (220 − age × .75 to .85) at least three times a week for at least 20 minutes. Encourage exercise as a means of reducing levels of stress and frustration.

    RP: _____

    _____

__. _____

    _____

    RP: _____

    _____

—. _____
   _____

RP: _____
   _____

—. _____
   _____

RP: _____
   _____

DIAGNOSTIC SUGGESTIONS

Axis I:	315.9	Learning Disorder NOS
	314.01	Attention-Deficit/Hyperactivity Disorder, Combined Type
	314.00	Attention-Deficit/Hyperactivity Disorder, Predominantly Inattentive Type
	314.01	Attention-Deficit/Hyperactivity Disorder, Predominantly Hyperactive-Impulsive Type
	314.9	Attention-Deficit/Hyperactivity Disorder NOS
	312.8	Conduct Disorder
	313.81	Oppositional Defiant Disorder
	312.9	Disruptive Behavior Disorder NOS
	291.8	Alcohol-Induced Mood Disorder
	292.xx	Substance-Induced Mood Disorder
	309.4	Adjustment Disorder with Mixed Disturbance of Emotions and Conduct
	312.30	Impulse-Control Disorder NOS
	_____	_____
	_____	_____
Axis II:	301.7	Antisocial Personality Disorder
	301.83	Borderline Personality Disorder
	_____	_____
	_____	_____

BORDERLINE TRAITS

BEHAVIORAL DEFINITIONS

1. Extreme emotional reactivity (anger, anxiety, or depression) under minor stress that usually does not last more than a few hours to a few days.
2. A pattern of intense, chaotic interpersonal relationships.
3. Marked identity disturbance.
4. Impulsive behaviors that are potentially self-damaging.
5. Recurrent suicidal gestures, threats, or self-mutilating behavior.
6. Chronic feelings of emptiness or boredom.
7. Frequent eruptions of intense, inappropriate anger.
8. Easily feels that others are treating him or her unfairly or that they can't be trusted.
9. Analyzes most issues in simple terms of right and wrong (black/white, trustworthy/deceitful) without regard for extenuating circumstances or complex situations.
10. Becomes very anxious with any hint of perceived abandonment in a relationship.

___. _____
    _____
___. _____
    _____
___. _____
    _____

LONG-TERM GOALS

1. Develop program of recovery from substance abuse that reduces the impact of borderline traits on sobriety.

2. Develop and demonstrate coping skills to deal with mood swings.
3. Develop the ability to control impulses.
4. Understand how borderline traits can foster a pattern of continued substance abuse.
5. Learn and demonstrate strategies to deal with dysphoric moods.
6. Modify dichotomous thinking.
7. Develop and demonstrate anger management skills.
8. Learn and practice interpersonal relationship skills.
9. Learn stress management skills.
10. Reduce the frequency of self-damaging behaviors (such as substance abuse, reckless driving, sexual acting out, binge eating, or suicidal behaviors).
11. Replace negative, self-defeating thinking with more realistic, self-enhancing self-talk.

—. _____
   _____
   _____

—. _____
   _____
   _____

—. _____
   _____

SHORT-TERM OBJECTIVES

1. Keep a daily feelings journal. (1)

2. Practice identifying and correcting self-defeating thinking. (1, 2, 3, 4, 5)

3. Keep a daily record of negative self-defeating thinking that leads to failure. (1, 2, 3, 4)

4. Make a list of positive, accurate self-statements to use in daily positive self-talk. (3, 4, 5)

THERAPEUTIC INTERVENTIONS

1. Assign patient to write a daily journal of emotions that were experienced, the feelings that developed, and actions that resulted from those feelings.

   RP:* _____

   _____

2. Help patient differentiate between self-defeating and self-enhancing behaviors.

   RP: _____

   _____

*RP = Responsible Professional

5. List five occasions when borderline traits have led to substance abuse. (6, 7, 8, 10)

6. Describe situations in which self-damaging behaviors such as substance abuse, reckless driving, sexual acting out, binge eating, or suicidal behaviors lead to negative consequences and list alternative adaptive behaviors. (6, 7, 10, 13)

7. Verbalize five reasons borderline traits are a problem in recovery. (6, 7, 8, 9, 10)

8. Verbalize how impulsivity has led to negative consequences. (8, 7, 10, 13)

9. Develop a written plan to decrease the frequency of sudden mood swings. (9, 11, 14, 15)

10. Practice the impulse-control skills of stopping, thinking, and planning before acting. (10, 12, 13, 17, 18)

11. Verbalize an understanding of how anger toward others or fear of abandonment is expressed in suicidal gestures or self-mutilating behavior. (13, 16, 19, 20, 21, 22)

12. Identify interpersonal situations that easily trigger feelings of anger or fear of abandonment. (13, 14, 15)

13. Verbalize the negative social consequences of frequent expressions of untamed anger. (14, 15)

3. Using cognitive techniques, help the patient see how negative, self-defeating thinking leads to negative consequences.

RP: _____

_____

4. Using cognitive techniques, help the patient correct self-defeating thinking and replace self-derogatory thinking with positive, self-enhancing statements.

RP: _____

_____

5. Assist patient in building a list of positive, reinforcing statements to use daily for self-enhancement.

RP: _____

_____

6. Help the patient see how poor impulse control and intense mood swings increase the probability of substance abuse.

RP: _____

_____

7. Review several self-damaging behaviors, such as substance abuse, reckless driving, sexual acting out, or suicidal behaviors, and help the patient discover what he/she could have done appropriately in each situation.

RP: _____

_____

14. Verbalize alternative, constructive ways to cope with feelings of anger or fear. (16, 18, 19)

15. Write a plan for modifying impulsive behaviors. (12, 16, 17, 18, 19)

16. Role-play expressing anger in a calm, assertive manner. (16, 17, 18, 19)

17. Five times this week, talk calmly to someone when feeling upset. (18, 19, 20)

18. Meet with the physician to be evaluated for possible pharmacological treatment. (21, 22)

19. Take medications as prescribed and report any side effects to appropriate professionals. (22, 23)

20. Practice the healthy communication skills by listening to others, using "I statements," and sharing feelings. (24, 25)

21. Verbalize what will help in developing a feeling of interpersonal safety. (24, 25, 26)

22. Verbalize five ways a higher power can assist in resolving dependency needs. (26)

23. List the good and bad points of five friends or family members. (27, 28)

24. Discuss how dichotomous thinking leads to interpersonal difficulties. (27, 28)

8. Assist the patient in defining the criteria for borderline traits and identify how each trait makes recovery more difficult.

RP: _____

_____

9. Help the patient develop and practice coping skills to deal with sudden dysphoric mood swings.

RP: _____

_____

10. Teach the patient how impulsivity leads to negative consequences and how self-control leads to positive consequences.

RP: _____

_____

11. Teach the patient how negative thinking, feeling, and acting leads to negative consequences. Then teach the patient how positive thinking leads to positive consequences.

RP: _____

_____

12. Teach patient self-control strategies (e.g., "stop, look, listen, and think") to control impulses.

RP: _____

_____

25. Practice relaxation techniques two times a day for 10 to 20 minutes. (16, 29)

26. Exercise at least three times a week for at least 20 minutes. (16, 30)

27. Write an aftercare program that lists resources to be used when feeling angry, abandoned, or depressed rather than reverting to substance use. (31)

__. _____
_____

__. _____
_____

__. _____
_____

13. Probe the relationship between the patient's feelings of anger and/or fear and the behavior of suicide attempts or self-mutilation.

RP: _____
_____

14. Assist the patient in identifying triggers for anger or fear of abandonment and possible historical causes for these feelings being so predominant.

RP: _____
_____

15. Help the patient understand the self-defeating, alienating consequences of frequently expressing anger and/or desperately clinging to others.

RP: _____
_____

16. Help the patient develop a list of constructive reactions to feelings of anger or fear that will reduce impulsive acting out of feelings. (Examples are writing about feelings, talking to counselor, delaying expression for 24 hours, tracing feelings to own background, substituting physical exercise, practicing a relaxation exercise.)

RP: _____
_____

17. Teach impulse-control skills
using role playing, behavior
rehearsal, and modeling.

RP: _____

_____

18. Model verbalization of
anger in a controlled,
respectful manner, delaying
the response, if necessary,
to gain more control. Ask
the patient to role-play
calm anger expression.

RP: _____

_____

19. Help the patient make a list
of the people to call or visit
when he/she becomes upset,
then role-play several situations where the patient dis-
cusses a problem calmly.

RP: _____

_____

20. Assign the patient the task
of talking to someone
calmly when feeling angry,
fearful, or depressed.

RP: _____

_____

21. Physician to evaluate if
psychopharmacological
intervention is warranted.

RP: _____

_____

22. Physician to prescribe and adjust medication to maximize effects and reduce side effects.

    RP: _____

    _____

23. Staff to administer medications as ordered by physician and monitor for compliance, effectiveness, and side effects.

    RP: _____

    _____

24. Teach the patient how to listen, use "I statements," and share feelings.

    RP: _____

    _____

25. Assist the patient in developing healthy self-talk and good communication skills as a means of increasing feelings of interpersonal safety.

    RP: _____

    _____

26. Teach the patient about the higher-power concept in AA/NA and give examples about how the patient can turn problems over to the higher power in recovery.

    RP: _____

    _____

27. Assist the patient in understanding how dichotomous thinking leads to feelings of interpersonal mistrust, helping him/her to see positive *and* negative traits in all people.

    RP: _____

    _____

28. Challenge the extremes of the patient's thinking as it relates to decisions about good/bad, trustworthy/deceitful people.

    RP: _____

    _____

29. Using techniques such as progressive relaxation, teach the patient how to relax.

    RP: _____

    _____

30. Help the patient develop an exercise program that will help reduce stress levels.

    RP: _____

    _____

31. Assist the patient in developing a structured aftercare program that lists resources he/she can use when feeling angry, anxious, abandoned, or depressed.

    RP: _____

    _____

—. _____

_____

RP: _____

_____

—. _____

_____

RP: _____

_____

—. _____

_____

RP: _____

_____

DIAGNOSTIC SUGGESTIONS

Axis I: 296.xx   Major Depressive Disorder
               300.4   Dysthymic Disorder
               296.xx   Bipolar I Disorder
               296.89   Bipolar II Disorder
               309.81   Posttraumatic Stress Disorder
               313.82   Identity Problem

               _____   _____

Axis II: 301.83   Borderline Personality Disorder
               301.50   Histrionic Personality Disorder
               301.22   Schizotypal Personality Disorder
               301.7   Antisocial Personality Disorder
               301.0   Paranoid Personality Disorder
               301.81   Narcissistic Personality Disorder
               301.6   Dependent Personality Disorder

               _____   _____

               _____   _____

CHILDHOOD TRAUMA

BEHAVIORAL DESCRIPTIONS

1. History of childhood physical, sexual, or emotional abuse.
2. Unresolved psychological conflicts caused by childhood abuse or neglect.
3. Irrational fears, suppressed rage, low self-esteem, identity conflicts, depression, or anxious insecurity related to painful early life experiences.
4. Use of substance abuse to escape emotional pain tied to childhood abuse.
5. Intrusive memories, guilt, or emotional numbing from early childhood trauma.
6. Unresolved emotions and maladaptive behavior that is the result of childhood trauma.
7. Inability to trust others, bond in relationships, communicate effectively, and maintain healthy interpersonal relationships because of early childhood neglect or abuse.

__. _____
_____
__. _____
_____
__. _____
_____

LONG-TERM GOALS

1. Resolve conflictual feelings associated with painful childhood traumas and terminate substance abuse that has been used as a means of coping with those unresolved feelings.

2. Develop an awareness of how childhood issues have contributed to substance abuse.
3. Learn how childhood trauma resulted in interpersonal problems and substance abuse.
4. Maintain a program of recovery free of substance abuse and the negative effects of childhood trauma.
5. Learn to forgive perpetrators and turn them over to a higher power.
6. Resolve past childhood and family issues to alleviate fear, anger, and depression and to allow greater self-esteem and confidence.
7. Agree to attend a continuing care program to resolve past childhood trauma and substance abuse.

—. _____
   _____
   _____
—. _____
   _____
   _____
—. _____
   _____

SHORT-TERM OBJECTIVES

1. Verbalize powerlessness and unmanageability experienced as a child and directly relate these feelings to substance abuse. (1, 2)

2. Describe the traumatic experiences that were endured and the feelings of helplessness, rage, hurt, and sadness that resulted from those experiences. (1, 2, 3)

3. Identify the unhealthy rules and roles the patient learned in the family of origin. (2, 3)

THERAPEUTIC INTERVENTIONS

1. Using an AA step one exercise, help the patient see the powerlessness and unmanageability that resulted from using substance abuse to deal with the negative feelings associated with the childhood trauma.

   RP:*_____

   _____

2. Explore the painful experiences endured in the patient's family of origin and help identify the unhealthy emotional and

_____
*RP = Responsible Professional

4. Verbalize an understanding of how childhood abandonment, neglect, or abuse led to current interpersonal distrust, anger, low self-esteem, or depression. (4)

5. Identify a pattern of using drugs or alcohol as a means of escape from psychological pain associated with childhood traumas and verbalize more constructive means of coping. (1, 5)

6. Verbalize the unresolved grief tied to unmet needs, wishes, and wants of the childhood years. (6, 7)

7. Verbalize a plan to fulfill the unmet needs of childhood now that adulthood has been reached. (6, 7)

8. List the dysfunctional thoughts, feelings, and behaviors learned during the childhood trauma/ neglect; then replace each self-defeating thought with a new thought that is positive and self-enhancing. (7, 8)

9. Attend group therapy sessions to share thoughts and feelings related to childhood traumas and explain how substance abuse has been used to avoid negative feelings. (8, 9)

10. Share the feelings, thoughts, and behaviors that were used in the family of origin to protect self and endure the trauma. (10)

behavioral patterns that evolved from those experiences.

RP: _____

_____

3. Teach the patient about the unhealthy rules and roles that develop in dysfunctional families and help identify the role he/she played in the family dynamics.

RP: _____

_____

4. Help the patient understand the relationship between childhood trauma and current problems with trust, anger, self-esteem, or depression.

RP: _____

_____

5. Confront the behavior of substance abuse as a means of coping with emotional pain and assist in identifying the self-defeating, negative consequences of this behavior. Process healthier, constructive means of coping (sharing pain with others, attending AA meetings, confronting and then forgiving perpetrator, turning issue over to a higher power, etc.).

RP: _____

_____

11. Verbalize how the family of origin handled conflict; then practice healthy rules of conflict resolution. (10, 11)

12. List current maladaptive interpersonal relationship/communication skills and then develop and demonstrate new skills that are adaptive and healthy. (10, 11)

13. List five ways a higher power can assist in recovery from childhood trauma and substance abuse. (12)

14. Verbalize an understanding that perpetrators were wounded children, too, and begin to turn them over to the higher power. (12, 13)

15. Write a letter to the perpetrator detailing the childhood abuse and its effect on thoughts, feelings, and behavior. (14)

16. Write a letter to each primary caregiver describing the childhood abuse and current feelings, wishes, and wants. (15)

17. Learn and demonstrate honesty, openness, and assertiveness in communicating with others; practice these skills daily in recovery. (16, 17, 18)

18. Identify any patterns of repeating the abandonment, neglect, or abuse experienced as a child. (19)

6. Assist the patient in identifying, understanding, and verbalizing unresolved needs, wishes, and wants from the childhood years; then help him/her develop a written plan to meet each unmet need, wish, or want.

RP: _____

_____

7. Have the patient read *Healing the Shame That Binds You* (Bradshaw) and *Outgrowing the Pain* (Gil); then help him/her identify unresolved feelings, wishes, and wants.

RP: _____

_____

8. Probe the patient's childhood trauma/neglect and help him/her relate these events to current feelings, thoughts, and behaviors. Teach positive self-talk to replace negative messages.

RP: _____

_____

9. Direct group therapy sessions in which the patient is encouraged to share his/her story of childhood trauma, allowing for feedback of empathy, acceptance, and affirmation from group members.

RP: _____

_____

19. Verbalize an understanding of how the home group in AA/NA can provide a substitute for the healthy home the patient never experienced. (20)

20. Develop and agree to participate in an aftercare program to continue to recover from childhood abuse and substance abuse. (21)

—. _____
   _____
—. _____
   _____
—. _____
   _____

10. Explore the family reaction to conflict; then teach the patient the healthy conflict resolution skills of active listening, using "I messages," cooperation, compromise, and mutual respect.

    RP: _____
    _____

11. Help the patient identify the maladaptive relationship/communication skills learned as a child; then use modeling, role playing, and behavior rehearsal to teach him/her the healthy skills to use in recovery.

    RP: _____
    _____

12. Teach the patient about the AA/NA concept of a higher power and explain how the higher power can help him/her forgive others and reestablish self-esteem.

    RP: _____
    _____

13. Help the patient understand that oftentimes perpetrators were wounded children, too, and need to be forgiven and turned over to the higher power.

    RP: _____
    _____

14. Assign the patient to write a letter to his/her perpetrator detailing the emotional

trauma that resulted from
the abuse.

RP: _____

_____

15. Help the patient write a letter to each parent or primary caregiver detailing
the childhood abuse and
sharing what the patient
wants from each person in
recovery.

RP: _____

_____

16. Have the patient read *Taking Charge of Your Social
Life* (Gumbrill and Richey)
to enhance social communication skills. Process concepts in session.

RP: _____

_____

17. Teach the patient the
healthy communication
skills of being honest, asking for wants, and sharing
feelings.

RP: _____

_____

18. Using modeling, role playing, and behavior rehearsal,
teach the patient healthy,
assertive skills; then practice these skills in several
current problem situations.

RP: _____

_____

19. Explore the tendency to repeat a pattern of abuse and neglect toward the patient's own children when it has been experienced on a regular basis in childhood.

    RP: _____

    _____

20. Help the patient see that the new home AA/NA group can help substitute for a healthy home.

    RP: _____

    _____

21. Help the patient develop an aftercare program that includes regular attendance at recovery group meetings and the continued therapy necessary to recover from childhood trauma and substance abuse.

    RP: _____

    _____

__. _____

    _____

    RP: _____

    _____

__. _____

    _____

    RP: _____

    _____

___.___ _____

_____

RP: _____

_____

DIAGNOSTIC SUGGESTIONS

Axis I: 300.4   Dysthymic Disorder
              296.xx   Major Depressive Disorder
              300.02   Generalized Anxiety Disorder
              309.81   Posttraumatic Stress Disorder
              300.14   Dissociative Identity Disorder
              V61.21   Sexual Abuse of Child (995.5, Victim)
              V61.21   Physical Abuse of Child (995.5, Victim)
              V61.21   Neglect of Child (995.5, Victim)

              _____   _____

Axis II: 301.7   Antisocial Personality Disorder
              301.83   Borderline Personality Disorder
              301.6   Dependent Personality Disorder

              _____   _____

              _____   _____

DEPRESSION

BEHAVIORAL DEFINITIONS

1. Feels sad or down most days of the week.
2. Vegetative symptoms, including sleep disturbance, appetite disturbance, anhedonia, fatigue, weight change.
3. Persistent feelings of helplessness, hopelessness, worthlessness or guilt.
4. Loss of energy, excessive fatigue.
5. Poor concentration, indecisiveness.
6. Low self-esteem.
7. Mood-congruent hallucinations or delusions.
8. Engages in substance abuse as a means of escaping feelings of sadness, worthlessness, and helplessness.
9. Suicidal thoughts.
10. Expresses a wish to die without a suicidal thought or plan.

—. _____
   _____
   _____
—. _____
   _____
   _____
—. _____
   _____

LONG-TERM GOALS

1. Elevate mood and develop a program of recovery free from substance abuse.
2. Decrease dysfunctional thinking and increase positive, self-enhancing self-talk.

3. Understand affective disorder and how these symptoms make him or her vulnerable to substance abuse.
4. Develop a lifestyle full of pleasurable work, social activity, and play.
5. Improve physical functioning and develop a program of recovery that includes exercise, relaxation, and healthy eating and sleeping habits.
6. Improve social skills and develop a program of recovery that includes regular attendance at recovery groups.
7. Resolve interpersonal conflicts and grief.
8. Increase feelings of self-worth and self-esteem through learning how to help others.

—. _____
_____
—. _____
_____
—. _____
_____

SHORT-TERM OBJECTIVES

1. Verbalize the powerlessness and unmanageability that result from using substance abuse to cope with depression. (1, 2)
2. Verbalize an understanding of how depression leads to substance abuse and substance abuse leads to depression. (2)
3. Identify a pattern of using drugs or alcohol as a means of escape from depression, and verbalize more constructive means of coping. (3, 4)

THERAPEUTIC INTERVENTIONS

1. Using an AA step one exercise, help the patient admit powerlessness and unmanageability over substance abuse and depression.

   RP:* _____

   _____

2. Teach the patient that substance abuse results in negative psychological effects and that substance abuse is often used to control psy-

_____
*RP = Responsible Professional

4. Report no longer feeling the desire to take his/her life. (3, 5, 6)

5. State a desire to live and an end to wishes for death. (5, 6, 7)

6. Verbally identify the causes for depressed mood; develop positive statements and plans to cope with those causes. (6, 7)

7. Verbalize an understanding of how depression and substance abuse lead to a condition that AA/NA calls "insane." (2, 8)

8. List five ways a higher power can be useful in recovery from substance abuse and depression. (9)

9. Keep a daily record of dysfunctional thinking that includes each situation associated with depressed feelings and the thoughts that triggered those feelings. (10, 11)

10. Replace negative, self-defeating thinking with positive, accurate, self-enhancing self-talk. (10, 11)

11. Learn and demonstrate the ability to use positive conflict resolution skills to resolve interpersonal discord. (12, 13)

12. Visit with the physician to determine if psychopharmacological intervention is warranted, and take all medication as prescribed. (14, 15)

chological symptoms in a vicious cycle.

RP: _____

_____

3. Confront the behavior of substance abuse as a means of coping with depression and assist in identifying the self-defeating, negative consequences of this behavior.

RP: _____

_____

4. Process healthier, constructive means of coping with depression (sharing pain with others, attending AA meetings, developing positive cognitions, taking medication, turning conflicts over to a higher power, etc.).

RP: _____

_____

5. Assess and monitor suicidal potential, arranging for suicide precautions if necessary.

RP: _____

_____

6. Reinforce positive statements regarding life and the future.

RP: _____

_____

7. Assist patient in identifying causes for depression and develop positive cognitive messages and behavioral

13. Participate in a psychological assessment to determine the extent of depression and substance abuse. (16)

14. Verbalize unresolved grief and make a written plan to recover from grief issues. (17, 18, 19, 20)

15. Discuss the positives and negatives of the relationship with the deceased person and write a plan to develop new relationships. (18, 20)

16. Report an awareness of anger toward the deceased spouse or significant other for leaving. (18, 19)

17. Write a letter of good-bye to the person who was lost, sharing unresolved feelings. (20)

18. Write an autobiography detailing the exact nature of wrongs and turn past behavior over to a higher power. (21)

19. Read aloud ten positive, self-enhancing statements each morning. (22)

20. Encourage someone in recovery each day. Write down each incident and discuss with primary therapist. (23, 24)

21. Verbalize an understanding of how he/she is important to others in the recovery group. (23, 24)

actions to overcome those causes.

RP: _____

_____

8. Teach the patient about the AA/NA concept of insanity and relate this concept to the patient's substance abuse and depression.

RP: _____

_____

9. Explain the AA concept of a higher power and the ways in which a higher power can assist in recovery.

RP: _____

_____

10. Help the patient keep a daily record that lists each situation associated with the depressed feelings and the dysfunctional thinking that triggered the depression. Then use logic and reality to challenge each dysfunctional thought for accuracy, replacing it with a positive, accurate thought.

RP: _____

_____

11. Help the patient make a list of his/her negative self-defeating thinking and replace each thought with self-enhancing self-talk.

RP: _____

_____

22. Develop written plans and express hope for the future. (25)

23. Develop and implement an exercise program that includes training at a training heart rate $(220 - \text{age} \times .75$ to $.85)$ for at least 20 minutes at least three times a week. (26)

24. Write down five things each night for which he/she is grateful. (27)

25. Attend group therapy session to share thoughts and feelings related to depression and how substance abuse has been used to avoid these negative feelings. (28)

26. Develop an aftercare program that includes regular attendance at recovery groups and any therapy that the primary therapist deems appropriate. (29)

___. _____

_____

___. _____

_____

___. _____

_____

12. Teach the patient conflict resolution skills (e.g., empathy, active listening, "I messages," respectful communication, assertiveness without aggression, compromise); then use modeling, role playing, and behavior rehearsal to work through several current conflicts.

RP: _____

_____

13. In conjoint sessions, help the patient resolve interpersonal conflicts and problems.

RP: _____

_____

14. Physician will examine the patient and order medications as appropriate, titrate medications, and monitor for side effects.

RP: _____

_____

15. Medical staff will administer medications as prescribed by the physician and monitor for side effects and effectiveness.

RP: _____

_____

16. Psychologist will complete a psychological assessment to determine the extent of depression and make recommendations for treatment.

RP: _____

_____

17. Help the patient identify grief issues and develop a written plan for resolving grief (e.g., visit grave, write good-bye letter, attend support group, begin social activities, volunteer to help others).

    RP: _____

    _____

18. Probe the positive and negative elements of the patient's relationship with the deceased individual and help develop a plan for making new relationships.

    RP: _____

    _____

19. Encourage the patient to share the feelings of anger and resentment felt toward the significant other for leaving.

    RP: _____

    _____

20. Probe the patient's grief and help him/her say good-bye in a letter to the person lost.

    RP: _____

    _____

21. Using an AA fourth step inventory, assign the patient to write an autobiography detailing the exact nature of his/her wrongs; then help the

patient turn over past mis-
behavior to the higher
power.

RP: _____

_____

22. Help the patient develop
    ten accurate, self-enhancing
    statements to read each
    morning.

    RP: _____

    _____

23. Teach the patient the
    importance of helping
    others to build his/her own
    sense of self-worth and self-
    esteem; then assign patient
    to encourage someone in the
    program each day.

    RP: _____

    _____

24. Help the patient under-
    stand that he/she is needed
    in AA/NA to help others.
    Discuss how this builds self-
    esteem and self-worth.

    RP: _____

    _____

25. Assist the patient in devel-
    oping future plans, and
    show that these plans cre-
    ate new hope for tomorrow.

    RP: _____

    _____

26. Using current fitness levels,
    increase the patient's exer-
    cise by 10 percent each
    week until the patient is

exercising at a training
heart rate (220 − age × .75
to .85) for at least 20 minutes three times a week.

RP: _____

_____

27. Teach the patient about the
AA concept of "an attitude
of gratitude," and then
assign him/her to write
down five things he/she is
grateful for each day.

RP: _____

_____

28. Direct group therapy sessions in which the patient is
encouraged to share his/her
feelings of depression,
allowing for feedback of
empathy, acceptance, and
affirmation from group
members.

RP: _____

_____

29. Help the patient develop an
aftercare program that
includes regular attendance
at recovery groups and any
other therapy the patient
needs to improve health.

RP: _____

_____

__. _____

_____

RP: _____

_____

___.   _____

        _____

RP: _____

        _____

___.   _____

        _____

RP: _____

        _____

DIAGNOSTIC SUGGESTIONS

Axis I: 309.0   Adjustment Disorder With Depressed Mood
              309.28   Adjustment Disorder With Mixed Anxiety and
                       Depressed Mood
              311   Depressive Disorder NOS
              296.xx   Bipolar I Disorder
              296.89   Bipolar II Disorder
              300.4   Dysthymic Disorder
              301.13   Cyclothymic Disorder
              296.2x   Major Depressive Disorder, Single Episode
              296.3x   Major Depressive Disorder, Recurrent
              295.70   Schizoaffective Disorder
              310.1   Personality Change Due to (Axis III Disorder)
              V62.82   Bereavement

              _____   _____

Axis II: 301.83   Borderline Personality Disorder
              301.9   Personality Disorder NOS

              _____   _____

              _____   _____

FAMILY CONFLICTS

BEHAVIORAL DESCRIPTIONS

1. A pattern of family conflicts leading to dysfunctional relationships and substance abuse.
2. Repeated family physical fights, verbal arguments, or unresolved disputes.
3. Poor communication skills leading to an inability to solve family problems.
4. Physical or verbal abuse of family members.
5. Use of substance abuse to cope with feelings of anger, alienation, or depression related to conflict within the family.
6. Unresolved conflicts leading to an inability to love family members.
7. Long periods of noncommunication with family members due to unresolved conflicts.
8. A family that is not supportive to recovery.
9. Substance abuse in family members leading to a poor recovery environment.

—. _____
   _____
—. _____
   _____
—. _____
   _____

LONG-TERM GOALS

1. Maintain a program of recovery free of substance abuse and family conflict.

2. Learn and demonstrate healthy communication and conflict resolution skills leading to harmony within the family and cessation of substance abuse.
3. Resolve family conflicts and elicit the aid of family members in working on a stable program of recovery.
4. Terminate substance abuse and implement more healthy coping behaviors to deal with the conflicts within the family.
5. Begin to emancipate from the parents in a healthy way by making reasonable arrangements for independent living.
6. Understand the relationship between family conflicts and substance abuse.
7. Learn how the conflicts in the home of origin influence current family problems.
8. Learn and demonstrate healthy family interaction.
9. Forgive family members for the past and begin a life with each family member working his or her own program of recovery.

___. _____

_____

___. _____

_____

___. _____

_____

SHORT-TERM OBJECTIVES

1. Verbalize the powerlessness and unmanageability that resulted from using substance abuse to cope with family conflicts. (1, 2)

2. Verbalize an understanding of how family conflicts led to substance abuse and substance abuse led to family conflicts. (1, 2)

THERAPEUTIC INTERVENTIONS

1. Help the client see the powerlessness and unmanageability that resulted from using substance abuse to cope with family conflicts.

   RP:* _____

   _____

2. Assist the patient in understanding the vicious cycle that results from reacting to

*RP = Responsible Professional

3. Write a detailed account of current family conflicts and how they relate to conflicts in the family of origin experienced as a child. (2, 3)

4. Discuss how attempts to seize power and control do not lead to healthy interpersonal relationships. (3, 4)

5. Meet with family members to discuss current conflicts and make a written plan to resolve each issue. (2, 3, 5)

6. In a family session, verbalize how substance abuse fosters misunderstanding and conflict and conflict fosters substance abuse. (5, 6, 7)

7. Write a letter to each family member, taking the responsibility for the behavior of the past, stating feelings, and asking for what he/she would like from each member to support recovery. (8)

8. Listen to family members read letters sharing how they feel and stating what behavior they would like from the patient during his/her recovery. (9)

9. List which conflict resolution skills are going to be used when he/she is involved in a family argument. (10, 11, 12, 13)

10. List five ways a higher power can assist in recovery from family conflicts and substance abuse. (11)

family conflicts with substance abuse.

RP: _____

_____

3. Help the patient see the relationship between the family-of-origin childhood conflicts and current family conflicts; then assign him/her to write a detailed account of how the two are related.

RP: _____

_____

4. Teach the patient respect for independence and autonomy in a healthy family and help the patient see how power struggles lead to unresolved family conflict.

RP: _____

_____

5. In a family session, make a list of current family conflicts; then help the family make specific plans to resolve each issue.

RP: _____

_____

6. Help family members understand how family conflict increases the probability of substance abuse and how substance abuse increases the probability of family conflict.

RP: _____

_____

11. Practice the assertive communication formula "I feel . . . When you . . . I would prefer it if . . ." (12, 13, 14)

12. List instances when he/she shared feelings, wishes, and wants calmly and respectfully. (13, 14)

13. Verbalize the negative effects of passive or aggressive behaviors and list the positive effects of using assertive skills. (12, 13, 14)

14. Increase the level of independent functioning—finding and keeping a job, socializing with positive friends, finding own housing, etc. (15, 16)

15. Agree to continue to work on family conflict and substance abuse issues by regularly attending recovery groups and family therapy in aftercare. (17)

__. _____
   _____

__. _____
   _____

__. _____
   _____

7. Confront the patient when he/she blames others and does not accept responsibility for his/her own role in the family conflict.

   RP: _____
   _____

8. Help the patient write a letter to each family member, taking responsibility for problems in the past, sharing how he/she feels, and asking for what he/she would like from each family member to support his/her recovery.

   RP: _____
   _____

9. Help each family member write a letter to the patient stating how they feel and asking for what he/she would like from the patient during recovery. Ask each member to read the letter to the patient in a family session.

   RP: _____
   _____

10. Using modeling, role playing, and behavioral rehearsal, teach the patient what to do when he/she is in a family conflict (e.g., call someone; go to a meeting; use "I messages"; accept the responsibility for own behavior; don't blame; turn

it over to a higher power; stop, think, listen, and plan before acting).

RP: _____

_____

11. Explain the AA concept of a higher power and how this power can assist in resolving family conflicts and substance abuse.

RP: _____

_____

12. Teach the patient the assertive communication formula "I feel . . . When you . . . I would prefer it if . . ." Then practice the formula five times in role-playing current problem situations.

RP: _____

_____

13. Using modeling, role playing, and behavior rehearsal, teach the patient how to share feelings, wishes, and wants calmly in several difficult situations. Assign implementation with family members.

RP: _____

_____

14. Teach the patient the difference between passive, aggressive, and assertive behavior and assign him/

her to list the positive and negative effects of each method in conflict resolution.

RP: _____

_____

15. Probe the patient's fears surrounding emancipation.

RP: _____

_____

16. Confront emotional dependence and avoidance of economic responsibility that promotes a continuing pattern of dependently living off others.

RP: _____

_____

17. Help the patient develop an aftercare program that includes regular attendance at recovery groups and the family therapy that is necessary to resolve family conflicts and maintain abstinence.

RP: _____

_____

—. _____

_____

RP: _____

_____

—. _____

_____

RP: _____

_____

—. _____

_____

RP: _____

_____

DIAGNOSTIC SUGGESTIONS

Axis I:	313.81	Oppositional Defiant Disorder
	312.8	Conduct Disorder
	V61.20	Parent-Child Relational Problem
	V61.1	Partner Relational Problem
	V61.8	Sibling Relational Problem
	V62.81	Relational Problem NOS
	V71.01	Adult Antisocial Behavior
	V71.02	Child or Adolescent Antisocial Behavior
	_____	_____
	_____	_____
Axis II:	301.83	Borderline Personality Disorder
	301.7	Antisocial Personality Disorder
	301.6	Dependent Personality Disorder
	_____	_____
	_____	_____

GRIEF/LOSS UNRESOLVED

BEHAVIORAL DEFINITIONS

1. Unresolved bereavement resulting in substance abuse to cope with the grief.
2. Constant thoughts of the lost loved one to the point of inability to move forward in life to other plans or relationships.
3. Depression centered around a deceased loved one.
4. Excessive and unreasonable feelings of responsibility for the loss of a significant other, including believing that he/she did not do enough to prevent the person's death.
5. Feelings of guilt about being a survivor when loved ones have died.
6. Avoidance of talking about the death of a loved one on anything more than a superficial level.
7. Vegetative symptoms of depression (lack of appetite, weight loss, sleep disturbance, anhedonia, lack of energy).

—. _____
_____
_____
—. _____
_____
_____
—. _____
_____

LONG-TERM GOALS

1. Resolve feelings of anger, sadness, guilt, and/or abandonment surrounding the loss of the loved one and make plans for the future.
2. Accept the loss of the loved one and increase social contact with others.

3. Develop a plan for life, renewing old relationships and making new ones.
4. Maintain a program of recovery free from substance abuse and unresolved grief.
5. Let go of the deceased person and turn him/her over to a higher power.

—. _____

_____

—. _____

_____

—. _____

_____

SHORT-TERM OBJECTIVES

1. Tell the story of the lost relationship. (1)

2. Discuss the positive and negative aspects of the lost relationship. (1, 2)

3. Verbalize how the loss of the loved one led to substance abuse to avoid painful feelings. (3, 5, 7)

4. List several negative consequences that resulted from using substance abuse to cope with grief and loss. (3, 6)

5. Verbalize the feelings of anger, guilt, sadness, and/or abandonment caused by the loss. (4, 5, 7)

THERAPEUTIC INTERVENTIONS

1. Encourage the patient to share the entire story of the relationship with the lost person, possibly using pictures or mementos connected to the deceased loved one.

   RP:*_____

   _____

2. Help the patient see both the positive and negative aspects of the lost relationship, keeping him/her from overidealizing the relationship.

   RP: _____

   _____

_____

*RP = Responsible Professional

6. Verbalize why he/she should not feel guilty about the loss. (7, 11, 12)

7. Verbalize an understanding of how the dependence on the lost person and substance dependence are similar. (5, 7, 8)

8. Write a plan for living a more independent life. (9, 10, 14, 15)

9. List five ways a higher power can assist in recovery from grief and substance abuse. (10, 11, 13)

10. Verbalize an understanding of how the death of someone can be a part of God's plan for the patient. (10, 11)

11. Practice prayer and meditation each day, seeking God's help for living without the loved one and the power to carry that out. (10, 13)

12. Write a plan to increase social interaction with old friends and make new ones. (14, 15, 17)

13. Write a letter of good-bye to the lost loved one, sharing feelings and thoughts. (4, 7, 16)

14. Make contact with an AA/NA temporary sponsor and share plans for recovery. (17, 19)

15. Encourage at least one person in recovery each day. (18)

3. Identify how chemical use led to avoidance of working through the loss and how this avoidance has created negative consequences.

RP: _____

_____

4. Help the patient identify the feelings of hurt, loss, abandonment, and anger resulting from the loss.

RP: _____

_____

5. Teach the patient how the loss of the loved one led to substance abuse to cope with the pain.

RP: _____

_____

6. Show the patient how substance abuse led to more pain and unresolved feelings.

RP: _____

_____

7. Explore feelings of guilt and blame surrounding the loss.

RP: _____

_____

8. Help the patient see the common elements in the dependency on the deceased individual and chemical dependency.

RP: _____

_____

16. Develop a written aftercare plan (e.g., regularly attend recovery groups, get a sponsor, and continue the treatment necessary to resolve substance abuse and grief). (15, 19)

___. _____
   _____
___. _____
   _____
___. _____
   _____

9. Help the patient write a plan to help him/her live a more active and independent life (e.g., make plans for social life, hobbies, financial security, job, recovery; sponsor a grief group, a single's group, etc.).

RP: _____
_____

10. Explain the AA concept of a higher power and help the patient see how this can assist him/her in recovery from grief and substance abuse.

RP: _____
_____

11. Assign the patient to read page 449 in the *Big Book* of Alcoholics Anonymous and discuss how the loss of a loved one could be part of God's plan.

RP: _____
_____

12. Using logic and reasoning, help the patient see that he/she is not responsible for the loss.

RP: _____
_____

13. Using an AA step eleven exercise, teach the patient how to pray and meditate; then assign him/her to contact God each day about his/her grief.

    RP: _____

    _____

14. Assign the patient to write a plan to improve social contact with old friends and make new ones.

    RP: _____

    _____

15. Teach the patient the importance of regularly attending recovery groups, getting a sponsor, and helping others in recovery.

    RP: _____

    _____

16. Assign the patient to write a letter to the lost individual, sharing the unresolved feelings. Process the letter in a group or individual session.

    RP: _____

    _____

17. Assign the patient to make contact with an AA/NA temporary sponsor and discuss recovery plans.

    RP: _____

    _____

18. To improve self-worth and self-esteem, assign the patient to encourage one person in recovery each day.

   RP: _____

   _____

19. Help the patient develop a written aftercare plan that specifically outlines a recovery plan (e.g., attend AA/NA meetings and aftercare sessions, continue therapy, get a sponsor, turn it over daily, pray and meditate).

   RP: _____

   _____

___. _____

   _____

   RP: _____

   _____

___. _____

   _____

   RP: _____

   _____

___. _____

   _____

   RP: _____

   _____

DIAGNOSTIC SUGGESTIONS

Axis I:	296.2x	Major Depressive Disorder, Single Episode
	296.3x	Major Depressive Disorder, Recurrent
	311	Depressive Disorder NOS
	308.3	Acute Stress Disorder
	V62.82	Bereavement
	309.0	Adjustment Disorder With Depressed Mood
	309.3	Adjustment Disorder With Disturbance of Conduct
	309.24	Adjustment Disorder With Anxiety
	309.28	Adjustment Disorder With Mixed Anxiety and Depressed Mood
	309.4	Adjustment Disorder With Mixed Disturbance of Emotions and Conduct
	_____	_____
	_____	_____

IMPULSIVITY

BEHAVIORAL DESCRIPTIONS

1. A tendency to act impulsively, without careful deliberation, which results in numerous negative consequences.
2. Difficulty with patience, particularly while waiting for someone or waiting in line.
3. A pattern of impulsive substance abuse.
4. Loss of control over aggressive impulses, resulting in assault, self-destructive behavior, or damage to property.
5. Seems to want everything immediately—decreased ability to delay pleasure or gratification.
6. A history of acting out in at least two areas that are potentially self-damaging (e.g., financial carelessness, promiscuous sexual activity, reckless driving, substance abuse).
7. Overreactivity to mildly aversive or pleasure-oriented stimulation.
8. A sense of tension or affective arousal before engaging in the impulsive behavior (e.g., kleptomania or pyromania).
9. A sense of pleasure, gratification, or release at the time of committing the ego-dystonic act.

__. _____
_____
_____
__. _____
_____
__. _____
_____

LONG-TERM GOALS

1. Maintain a program of recovery free from impulsive behavior and substance abuse.
2. Reduce the frequency of impulsive behavior and increase the frequency of behavior that is carefully thought out.
3. Reduce thoughts that trigger impulsive behavior and increase self-talk that controls behavior.
4. Learn the techniques necessary to decrease impulsive thoughts, feelings, and behaviors and develop a program of recovery consistent with careful thoughts and behaviors.
5. Learn to stop, think, listen, and plan before acting.
6. Learn to reinforce self rather than depend on others for reward.

—. _____
_____
_____
—. _____
_____
—. _____
_____

SHORT-TERM OBJECTIVES

1. Verbalize an understanding of the powerlessness and unmanageability resulting from impulsivity and substance abuse. (1)

2. Discuss how impulsivity and substance abuse meet the AA criteria for insanity. (2)

3. Identify the negative consequences caused by impulsivity and substance abuse. (3, 4, 5, 6)

THERAPEUTIC INTERVENTIONS

1. Using an AA step one exercise, help the patient understand how impulsivity and substance abuse lead to powerlessness and unmanageability.

   RP:* _____
   _____

2. Using a AA step two exercise, help the patient see that doing the same things over and over again and

---
*RP = Responsible Professional

4. Verbally identify several occasions when impulsive action led to substance abuse and subsequent negative consequences. (4, 6)

5. Before acting on behavioral decisions, frequently review them with a trusted friend or family member for feedback regarding possible consequences. (7)

6. Verbalize the biopsychosocial elements that cause or exacerbate impulsivity and substance abuse. (8)

7. Comply with a physician evaluation regarding the necessity for psychopharmacological intervention and take all medications as prescribed. (9, 10)

8. Identify the thoughts that trigger impulsive behavior and substance abuse; then replace each one with a thought that is accurate, positive, self-enhancing, and adaptive. (11, 12)

9. Develop a list of accurate, positive, self-enhancing statements to read each day, particularly when feeling upset. (12)

10. List the inappropriate behaviors displayed when feeling anxious or uncomfortable and replace each behavior with an action that is positive and adaptive. (13, 15)

expecting different results meets the AA definition of insanity.

RP: _____

_____

3. Help patient make connections between his/her impulsivity and negative consequences experienced.

RP: _____

_____

4. Assign the patient to write a list of negative consequences that occurred because of impulsivity and substance abuse.

RP: _____

_____

5. Help the patient see how dangerous it is to act impulsively (e.g., you don't have time to consider consequences; you can't plan effectively).

RP: _____

_____

6. Explore impulsive actions by the patient that resulted in substance abuse and negative consequences.

RP: _____

_____

7. Conduct a session with spouse, significant other, sponsor, or family member and patient to develop a

11. List new ways to reinforce self without depending on others for reward. (14, 15)

12. Practice a relaxation exercise twice a day for 10 to 20 minutes; then practice relaxing when feeling upset or uncomfortable. (15)

13. Practice the assertive formula, "I feel . . . When you . . . I would prefer it if . . ." (16)

14. Identify situations where assertiveness has been implemented and describe the consequences. (17)

15. Practice stopping, thinking, listening, and planning before acting. (18, 19)

16. List instances where "stop, think, listen, and plan" has been implemented, citing the positive consequences. (19)

17. Verbalize an understanding of AA's step three regarding the role of a higher power and explain how this step can be used in recovery from impulsivity and substance abuse. (19, 20)

18. Write an autobiography detailing the exact nature of the patient's wrongs and relate each one to impulsivity and substance abuse. (21)

contract for receiving feedback prior to impulsive acts.

RP: _____

_____

8. Probe the patient's biopsychosocial history and help the patient see the precipitants of his/her impulsivity and substance abuse.

RP: _____

_____

9. Physician will examine the patient, order medications as indicated, titrate medications, and monitor for side effects.

RP: _____

_____

10. Staff will administer the medications as ordered by the physician and monitor for side effects and effectiveness.

RP: _____

_____

11. Help the patient uncover dysfunctional thoughts that lead to impulsivity and substance abuse; then replace each of these with a thought that is accurate, positive, self-enhancing, and adaptive.

RP: _____

_____

19. Develop and write a continuing care program that includes the recovery group meetings and any further therapy necessary for recovery. (22)

___. _____

_____

___. _____

_____

___. _____

_____

12. Help the patient develop a list of positive, accurate, self-enhancing thoughts to read each day, particularly when feeling upset or uncomfortable.

RP: _____

_____

13. Probe the patient's anxious behaviors and then use modeling, role playing, and behavior rehearsal to teach the patient new behaviors that are positive and adaptive (e.g., talking to someone about the problem, taking a time-out, calling the sponsor, going to a meeting, exercising, relaxing).

RP: _____

_____

14. Help the patient see the importance of rewarding him-/herself (using hobbies, relaxation, games, sports, social activities, meetings, etc.) so as not to depend on others for reward.

RP: _____

_____

15. Using relaxation techniques such as progressive relaxation, self-hypnosis, or biofeedback, teach the patient how to relax completely; then have the patient relax whenever he/she feels uncomfortable.

RP: _____

_____

16. Using modeling, role playing, and behavior rehearsal, show the patient how to use the assertive formula "I feel . . . When you . . . I would prefer it if . . ." in difficult situations.

    RP: _____

    _____

17. Review implementation of assertiveness and feelings about it as well as the consequences of it.

    RP: _____

    _____

18. Using modeling, role playing, and behavior rehearsal, teach the patient how to use "stop, think, listen, and plan before acting" in several current situations.

    RP: _____

    _____

19. Review the use of "stop, think, listen, and plan" in day-to-day living and identify the positive consequences.

    RP: _____

    _____

20. Using an AA step three exercise, teach the patient how to turn his/her will and life over to the care of the higher power and discuss how this step can be beneficial in recovery.

    RP: _____

    _____

21. Explain the AA concept of a higher power and discuss how the patient can use a higher power effectively in recovery.

    RP: _____

    _____

22. Using an AA step four exercise, have the patient write an autobiography explaining exact nature of his/her wrongs and relating these wrongs to impulsivity and substance abuse.

    RP: _____

    _____

23. Help the patient develop an aftercare plan (e.g., regularly attend recovery groups, get a sponsor, and seek any further therapy as necessary to recover from impulsivity and substance abuse).

    RP: _____

    _____

__. _____

    _____

    RP: _____

    _____

__. _____

    _____

    RP: _____

    _____

___. _____

_____

RP: _____

_____

DIAGNOSTIC SUGGESTIONS

Axis I:
312.8	Conduct Disorder
313.81	Oppositional Defiant Disorder
309.3	Adjustment Disorder With Disturbance of Conduct
312.34	Intermittent Explosive Disorder
314	Attention-Deficit/Hyperactivity Disorder
312.9	Disruptive Behavior Disorder NOS
312.30	Impulse-Control Disorder NOS
V71.01	Adult Antisocial Behavior
V71.02	Child or Adolescent Antisocial Behavior
____	_____

Axis II:
301.7	Antisocial Personality Disorder
301.83	Borderline Personality Disorder
301.81	Narcissistic Personality Disorder
____	_____
____	_____

LEGAL PROBLEMS

BEHAVIORAL DESCRIPTIONS

1. Legal charges pending adjudication.
2. History of repeated violations of the law, many of which occurred while under the influence of drugs or alcohol.
3. Unresolved legal problems complicating recovery from substance abuse.
4. Fears of the legal system adjudicating current problems.
5. History of repeated violations of the law buying, selling, or using illegal substances.
6. Court-ordered treatment for substance abuse.
7. Pending divorce accompanied by anger, resentment, and fear of abandonment.
8. Chemical dependency that has resulted in several arrests.
9. Fear of loss of freedom due to current legal charges.

__. _____
   _____

__. _____
   _____

__. _____
   _____

LONG-TERM GOALS

1. Maintain a program of recovery free from substance abuse and legal conflicts.
2. Accept the responsibility for legal problems without blaming others.

3. Consult legal authorities (attorney, probation officer, police, court official, etc.) to make plans for adjudicating legal conflicts.
4. Understand the role of abstinence in avoiding negative consequences that include legal problems.

—. _____
    _____
    _____
—. _____
    _____
    _____
—. _____
    _____

SHORT-TERM OBJECTIVES

1. Verbalize the powerlessness and unmanageability that results from legal conflicts and substance abuse. (1, 2, 3)

2. Verbalize an acceptance of the responsibility for substance abuse and legal problems without blaming others. (1, 2, 3)

3. Admit responsibility for illegal activity and connect this behavior to substance abuse. (2, 3)

4. Write a plan outlining the changes needed in behavior, attitude, and associates to protect self from harmful legal consequences. (4)

THERAPEUTIC INTERVENTIONS

1. Help the patient understand the relationship between substance abuse and legal conflicts and explore how these problems result in powerlessness and unmanageability.

   RP:*_____

   _____

2. Help the patient identify and accept responsibility for the many decisions he/she made that resulted in substance abuse and legal problems without blaming others.

   RP: _____

   _____

_____

*RP = Responsible Professional

5. Identify and verbalize the tendency to become involved in legal conflicts when high, intoxicated, or in withdrawal. (2, 3, 5)

6. Identify the negative emotional states associated with illegal activity and substance abuse. (5, 6)

7. Meet with an attorney to make plans for resolving legal conflicts. (7)

8. Contact the probation/ parole officer and agree in writing to meet the conditions of probation/ parole. (8)

9. Verbalize ways to meet social, emotional, and financial needs in recovery without illegal activity or substance abuse. (9, 16)

10. Identify the antisocial behaviors and attitudes that contributed to legal conflicts and learn prosocial behaviors. (10, 11, 12)

11. Verbalize the importance of obeying the laws of society to maintain abstinence and work on a program of recovery. (9, 10, 11)

12. Identify and correct the criminal thinking that led to legal conflicts and substance abuse. (6, 12)

13. Verbalize the importance of helping others to maintain recovery. (13)

3. Confront the patient with his/her avoidance of responsibility for the legal problems and substance abuse.

   RP: _____

   _____

4. Help the patient make a plan to honestly protect him-/herself from possible adverse consequences of legal problems by living within the law and associating with law-abiding people.

   RP: _____

   _____

5. Help the patient see the relationship between substance abuse and illegal activity.

   RP: _____

   _____

6. Probe the thoughts and feelings that surround substance abuse and legal problems and make plans to resolve each dysfunctional thought and feeling.

   RP: _____

   _____

7. Encourage and facilitate the patient meeting with an attorney to discuss plans for resolving legal conflicts.

   RP: _____

   _____

14. Verbalize the importance of a higher power in recovery and list five ways that a higher power can assist in recovery. (7, 14)

15. Develop an aftercare program that includes regular attendance at recovery groups and any other necessary therapy. (15)

16. Verbalize the importance of resolving legal issues honestly. (9, 16)

__. _____

_____

__. _____

_____

__. _____

_____

8. Help the patient meet with his/her probation/parole officer and assign patient to agree in writing to meet all conditions of probation/parole.

RP: _____

_____

9. Help the patient develop a plan to meet social, emotional, and financial needs in recovery without resorting to criminal activity or substance abuse.

RP: _____

_____

10. Teach the patient the difference between antisocial and prosocial behaviors, helping to identify his/her antisocial behaviors and attitudes. Then help develop prosocial plans in recovery (e.g., respect for the law, helping others, honesty, reliability, regular attendance at work, recovery groups, aftercare, halfway house).

RP: _____

_____

11. Help the patient understand why he/she needs to obey the law in order to maintain abstinence.

RP: _____

_____

12. Explain the dynamics of criminal thinking (rationalization, denial, superoptimism, blaming others, etc.). Help the patient identify his/her criminal thinking, replacing each criminal thought with one that is honest and respectful of others.

    RP: _____

    _____

13. Help the patient understand the importance of helping others in recovery in order to replace an attitude of taking with an attitude of giving and self-sacrifice.

    RP: _____

    _____

14. Explain the AA/NA concept of a higher power and discuss how it can assist in recovery from legal conflicts and substance abuse.

    RP: _____

    _____

15. Help the patient develop an aftercare program that has all of the elements necessary to maintain abstinence and resolve legal conflicts.

    RP: _____

    _____

16. Help the patient understand the importance of
resolving legal conflicts
honestly and legally.

RP: _____

_____

___. _____

_____

RP: _____

_____

___. _____

_____

RP: _____

_____

___. _____

_____

RP: _____

_____

DIAGNOSTIC SUGGESTIONS

Axis I:	312.8	Conduct Disorder
	313.81	Oppositional Defiant Disorder
	309.3	Adjustment Disorder With Disturbance of Conduct
	312.34	Intermittent Explosive Disorder
	V71.01	Adult Antisocial Behavior
	V71.02	Child or Adolescent Antisocial Behavior
	_____	_____
	_____	_____
Axis II:	301.7	Antisocial Personality Disorder
	301.83	Borderline Personality Disorder
	301.81	Narcissistic Personality Disorder
	_____	_____
	_____	_____

LIVING-ENVIRONMENT DEFICIENCY

BEHAVIORAL DEFINITIONS

1. Currently living in an environment in which there is a high risk for relapse.
2. Lives with an individual who is a regular user/abuser of alcohol or drugs.
3. Social life is characterized by significant social isolation or withdrawal.
4. Living in an environment in which there is a high risk of physical, sexual, or emotional abuse.
5. Friends or relatives are addicted.
6. Family is angry or negative toward the addict and not supportive of a recovery program.
7. Financially destitute and needs assistance for adequate food and shelter.
8. Peer group members are regular users/abusers of alcohol or drugs.
9. Lives in a neighborhood that has a high incidence of alcohol and drug addiction as well as crime.

—. _____
   _____
—. _____
   _____
—. _____
   _____

LONG-TERM GOALS

1. Maintain a program of recovery free from substance abuse and the negative impact of the deficient environment.

2. Improve the social, occupational, financial, and living situation sufficiently to increase the probability of a successful recovery from substance abuse.
3. Understand the negative impact of the current environment on substance abuse recovery.
4. Develop a peer group that is supportive of recovery.
5. Motivate family members to be supportive of recovery.
6. Work on a program of recovery that necessitates attendance at recovery groups and helping others.

—. _____
_____
—. _____
_____
—. _____
_____

SHORT-TERM OBJECTIVES

1. Verbalize the sense of powerlessness and unmanageability that results from a deficient environment and substance abuse. (1, 2, 3, 4)

2. Discuss specific living-environment problems as they negatively affect recovery. (2, 3, 4)

3. List several occasions when the living-environment deficit led to negative consequences and substance abuse. (2, 3, 4)

4. Explain how the current peer/family group increases the risk for relapse. (2, 3, 4)

THERAPEUTIC INTERVENTIONS

1. Using an AA step one exercise, help the patient see the powerlessness and unmanageability that results from substance abuse and a deficient environment.

   RP:*_____

   _____

2. Help the patient identify problems in the living environment and explore the negative impact they will have on recovery.

   RP: _____

   _____

---

*RP = Responsible Professional

5. List the specific living-environment problems and write a plan to address each one in recovery. (5, 6, 7, 8)

6. Identify current social/occupational/financial needs and make a plan to meet each need in recovery. (7, 8)

7. List ten reasons to become involved in a new peer group that is supportive of recovery. (4, 8, 11)

8. Meet with an AA/NA contact person to discuss plans for recovery. (9, 11)

9. Write a personal recovery plan detailing the recovery groups, aftercare, and further treatment the patient is going to need in recovery. (10, 11, 12)

10. Write a plan for developing contacts with people who attend recovery meetings. (10, 11)

11. List the ways in which a higher power can assist in recovery from a deficient living environment and substance abuse. (12, 13)

12. Practice turning over living-environment problems and cravings to God. (12, 13, 17)

13. Complete an AA fourth-step inventory outlining the exact nature of the wrongs; then share the inventory with someone in recovery. (14)

3. Help the patient list specific instances in which living-environment problems led to negative consequences and substance abuse.

   RP: _____

   _____

4. Explain the importance of the peer/family group in recovery and help the patient see how his/her current environment is a high-risk situation.

   RP: _____

   _____

5. Help the patient identify each living-environment problem and assist in writing a plan to address each problem in recovery.

   RP: _____

   _____

6. Discuss the alternatives available for moving out of current living situation that promotes ongoing substance abuse.

   RP: _____

   _____

7. Help the patient identify his/her social/occupational/financial needs and write a plan to meet each need in recovery.

   RP: _____

   _____

14. Write a letter to each significant other, discussing the problems with the living environment and sharing plans for recovery. (15, 16)

15. In a family session, discuss current living-environment problems and make plans for recovery. (15, 16, 17)

16. Develop a written plan to establish how to react to family members who are addicted. (17)

17. Verbalize a plan to continue spiritual growth within a community of believers. (12, 18)

18. Practice drug-refusal exercises in risk situations. (19)

—. _____
   _____

—. _____
   _____

—. _____
   _____

8. Discuss the importance of a supportive peer group and have patient list ten reasons he/she needs a new peer group to maintain abstinence.

   RP: _____

   _____

9. Facilitate the patient meeting with an AA/NA contact person and encourage him/her to discuss recovery plans.

   RP: _____

   _____

10. Help the patient develop a personal recovery plan that has all of the elements necessary to recover from substance abuse and the deficient living environment.

    RP: _____

    _____

11. Teach the patient the importance of developing a new peer group and encourage attendance at AA/NA meetings with others in the program.

    RP: _____

    _____

12. Explain the AA concept of a higher power and show the patient how the higher power can assist in recovery.

    RP: _____

    _____

13. Using an AA step three exercise, teach the patient how to turn over his/her will and life to God.

    RP: _____

    _____

14. Using an AA step four inventory, assign the patient to write an autobiography stating the exact nature of his/her wrongs; then encourage sharing the inventory with someone in recovery.

    RP: _____

    _____

15. Help the patient write a letter to each significant other sharing his/her problem with substance abuse, the ways in which the living environment has fostered the substance abuse, and the plan for recovery.

    RP: _____

    _____

16. Meet with family members to teach them about addiction, discuss the living-environment deficiencies, and make plans for support of the patient's recovery.

    RP: _____

    _____

17. Help the patient develop a plan to deal with family members who are addicted.

RP: _____

_____

18. Help the patient develop a plan to continue his/her spiritual growth (e.g., attend church, join recovery groups, get counseling; meet with pastor; read spiritual material).

RP: _____

_____

19. Using modeling, role playing, and behavior rehearsal, teach the patient how to say no to drugs and alcohol in high-risk situations.

RP: _____

_____

__. _____

_____

RP: _____

_____

__. _____

_____

RP: _____

_____

__. _____

_____

RP: _____

_____

DIAGNOSTIC SUGGESTIONS

Axis I:	V61.20	Parent-Child Relational Problem
	V61.1	Partner Relational Problem
	V61.8	Sibling Relational Problem
	V62.81	Relational Problem NOS
	V61.21	Physical Abuse of Child
	V61.21	Sexual Abuse of Child
	V61.21	Neglect of Child
	V61.1	Physical Abuse of Adult
	V61.1	Sexual Abuse of Adult
	V62.2	Occupational Problem
	V62.89	Religious or Spiritual Problem
	V62.4	Acculturation Problem
	_____	_____
	_____	_____

MANIA/HYPOMANIA

BEHAVIORAL DESCRIPTIONS

1. A distinct period of persistently elevated or irritable mood lasting at least four days.
2. Inflated sense of self-esteem and an exaggerated, euphoric belief in capabilities that denies any self-limitations or realistic obstacles, but sees others as standing in the way.
3. Decreased need for sleep.
4. More talkative than normal—pressured speech.
5. Racing thoughts.
6. Poor attention span and susceptibility to distraction.
7. An increase in initiating projects at home, work, or school—but without completion of tasks.
8. Excessive activities that are potentially self-damaging (e.g., buying sprees, sexual acting out, foolish business investments).
9. Impulsive use of drugs or alcohol without regard for consequences.
10. Verbal and/or physical aggression coupled with tantrumlike behavior (e.g., breaking things explosively) if wishes are blocked, in contrast to an earlier pattern of obedience and restraint.

—. _____

_____

—. _____

_____

—. _____

_____

LONG-TERM GOALS

1. Maintain a program of recovery free of manic/hypomanic behavior and substance abuse.
2. Increase the control over impulses, reduce the energy level, and stabilize the mood.
3. Reduce agitation, irritability, and pressured speech.
4. Increase rational thinking and behavior.
5. Understand the relationship between manic/hypomanic states and substance abuse.
6. Moderate mood and goal-directed behavior.
7. Understand the biopsychosocial aspects of manic/hypomanic states and substance abuse and accept the need for continued treatment.
8. Terminate substance abuse and take medications for mania on a consistent basis.

—. _____
_____

—. _____
_____

—. _____
_____

SHORT-TERM OBJECTIVES

1. Verbalize an understanding of the signs and symptoms of mania/hypomania and relate bipolar disease to substance abuse. (1, 2)

2. List several specific instances in which manic/hypomanic states led to substance abuse. (1, 2, 3, 5)

3. Verbalize the sense of powerlessness and unmanageability that results from

THERAPEUTIC INTERVENTIONS

1. Teach the patient the signs and symptoms of mania/hypomania and illustrate how it can foster substance abuse.

   RP:*_____

   _____

2. Explore the patient's chemical use history and identify instances in which manic/

_____

*RP = Responsible Professional

mania/hypomania and the accompanying use of substance abuse to cope with the impulsivity and mood swings. (1, 2, 3, 4)

4. Verbalize an understanding of the biopsychosocial correlates of mania/hypomania and substance abuse. (3, 4, 5)

5. List several negative consequences that resulted from untreated mania/hypomania and substance abuse. (5, 6)

6. Verbalize an understanding that manic/hypomanic states and substance abuse meet the AA criteria for insanity. (6)

7. Verbalize five ways a higher power can assist in recovery from manic/hypomanic states and substance abuse. (7, 8)

8. Practice turning over at least one problem to the higher power each day. Record the situation and discuss with the primary therapist. (7, 8)

9. Meet with the physician to see if psychopharmacological intervention is warranted, and take all medication as directed. (9)

10. Verbalize an acceptance of the necessity for continued medical monitoring for manic/hypomanic states. (9, 10, 11)

hypomanic states led to substance abuse.

RP: _____

_____

3. Using an AA step one exercise, help the patient see the powerlessness and unmanageability that results from mania/hypomania and the use of substance abuse to cope.

RP: _____

_____

4. Teach the patient the biopsychosocial correlates of mania/hypomania and substance abuse.

RP: _____

_____

5. Help the patient identify the negative consequences of mania/hypomania and substance abuse.

RP: _____

_____

6. Explain the AA concept of insanity, and help the patient understand how manic/hypomanic states and substance abuse meet the AA criteria for insanity.

RP: _____

_____

7. Explain the AA/NA concept of a higher power and encourage the patient to

11. Achieve mood stability by becoming slower to react with anger, less expansive, and more socially appropriate and sensitive. (9, 12, 13, 14, 15)

12. Decrease grandiose statements and express him/herself more realistically. (9, 12, 13)

13. Terminate self-destructive behaviors such as promiscuity, substance abuse, and the expression of overt hostility or aggression. (9, 14, 15)

14. Accept the limits set on manipulative and hostile behaviors that attempt to control others. (9, 12, 15)

15. Speak more slowly and be more subject-focused. (9, 13, 18)

16. Dress and groom in a less attention-seeking manner. (13, 19)

17. Identify positive traits and behaviors that build genuine self-esteem. (19)

18. Develop a personal recovery plan that includes all of the elements necessary to control mania/hypomania and to recover from substance abuse. (20, 25)

19. Educate the family members about the manic/hypomanic state and its relationship to substance abuse. Discuss how each member of the family is

use that higher power to help restore him/her to sanity.

RP: _____

_____

8. Using an AA step three exercise, teach the patient how to turn problems over to the higher power.

RP: _____

_____

9. Physician will examine the patient, order medications as indicated, titrate medications, and monitor for effectiveness and side effects.

RP: _____

_____

10. Staff will administer medications as ordered by the physician and monitor for side effects and effectiveness.

RP: _____

_____

11. Help the patient understand the importance of consistent medical management of manic/hypomanic states.

RP: _____

_____

12. Confront the patient's grandiosity and demandingness gently but firmly.

RP: _____

_____

going to work on a program of recovery. (21)

20. Write an AA fourth-step inventory and share with someone in recovery. (22)

21. Verbalize the importance of consistently attending recovery groups and of helping others in recovery. (23, 24)

22. Meet with an AA/NA contact person and discuss manic/hypomanic states and substance abuse. (24)

23. Agree to continue treatment in an environment that will help control mania/hypomania and substance abuse. (20, 23, 25)

___. _____
    _____

___. _____
    _____

___. _____
    _____

13. Repeatedly focus on the consequences of behavior to reduce thoughtless impulsivity.

    RP: _____

    _____

14. Facilitate impulse control by using role play, behavioral rehearsal, and role reversal to increase sensitivity to the consequences of behavior.

    RP: _____

    _____

15. Set limits on manipulation or acting out by making rules and establishing clear consequences for breaking them.

    RP: _____

    _____

16. Provide structure and focus for the patient's thoughts and actions by regulating the direction of conversation and establishing plans for behavior.

    RP: _____

    _____

17. Verbally reinforce slower speech and more deliberate thought processes.

    RP: _____

    _____

18. Encourage and reinforce appropriate dress and grooming.

    RP: _____

    _____

19. Help the patient identify strengths and assets to build self-esteem and confidence.

    RP: _____

    _____

20. Outline with the patient the steps necessary to manage manic/hypomanic states and substance abuse (e.g., take medication, comply with medical monitoring, continue therapy, regularly attend recovery groups, use the higher power, get a sponsor, help others in recovery).

    RP: _____

    _____

21. In a family session, help the patient educate the family members about mania/ hypomania and substance abuse; then help each family member develop a personal program of recovery.

    RP: _____

    _____

22. Using an AA fourth-step inventory, assign the patient to write an auto-

biography and share it with someone in recovery.

RP: _____

_____

23. Teach the patient the importance of working on a program of recovery that includes regularly attending recovery group meetings and helping others.

RP: _____

_____

24. Help the patient meet an AA/NA contact person and assign him/her to talk about manic/hypomanic states and substance abuse.

RP: _____

_____

25. Discuss discharge planning and help the patient decide on the kind of environment he/she needs in early recovery.

RP: _____

_____

__. _____

_____

RP: _____

_____

__. _____

_____

RP: _____

_____

—.   _____

_____

RP: _____

_____

DIAGNOSTIC SUGGESTIONS

Axis I: 296.xx   Bipolar I Disorder
296.89   Bipolar II Disorder
301.13   Cyclothymic Disorder
295.70   Schizoaffective Disorder
296.80   Bipolar Disorder NOS
310.1   Personality Change Due to (Axis III Disorder)
_____   _____
_____   _____

MEDICAL ISSUES

BEHAVIORAL DEFINITIONS

1. Patient has biomedical problems that complicate recovery from substance abuse.
2. There are medical problems that require medical monitoring of medications or assistance with mobility.
3. Use of mood-altering chemicals has resulted in organic brain syndrome that compromises learning.
4. Patient is not capable of self-administering prescribed medications.
5. Chronic pain syndrome places the patient at high risk for relapse.
6. Biomedical problems require medical/nursing assistance.
7. Patient uses mood-altering chemicals to self-medicate medical problems.
8. Negative emotions surrounding medical illness lead to substance abuse.
9. Medical problems are so severe the patient cannot concentrate on recovery.

___. _____
_____
___. _____
_____
___. _____
_____

LONG-TERM GOALS

1. Maintain a program of recovery free of substance abuse and the negative effects of medical issues.
2. Treat medical problems and return to normal levels of functioning.
3. Understand the relationship between medical issues and substance abuse.
4. Reduce the impact of medical problems on recovery and relapse potential.
5. With organic brain syndrome, improve the coping skills to levels that allow retention of a self-directed program of recovery.
6. Understand and participate in medical management of biomedical problems.
7. Reduce medical issue's influence on relapse potential.
8. Treat the medical problems to reduce the negative influence on recovery.

___. _____
_____
___. _____
_____
___. _____
_____

SHORT-TERM OBJECTIVES

1. Verbalize the powerlessness and unmanageability that result from using substances to cope with medical problems. (1, 2, 3)

2. Verbalize how the medical problems relate to substance abuse. (1, 2, 3)

3. Verbalize an acceptance of the seriousness of medical

THERAPEUTIC INTERVENTIONS

1. Using an AA step one exercise, help the patient see the powerlessness and unmanageability that result from medical issues and substance abuse.

RP:*_____

_____

---

*RP = Responsible Professional

problems and substance abuse. (2, 3, 4)

4. Verbalize an understanding of the medical problem and the need for medical management. (3, 4)

5. List the negative consequences that resulted from using substance abuse to cope with medical problems. (5)

6. Visit with the physician for examination of medical issues and substance abuse and cooperate with all treatment plans. (6, 7, 8)

7. Discuss with the physician the medical issues and substance abuse, including treatment plans and follow-up. (6, 7, 8, 9)

8. Participate in medical management of biomedical problems and substance abuse. (6, 7, 8, 9)

9. Verbalize an understanding of substance abuse as a contributing factor in the development of the medical problem. (8, 9)

10. Verbalize the importance of medical management in continuing care. (8, 9, 10)

11. List ten things the patient can do to improve physical functioning. (9, 11)

12. Cooperate in the administration of a psychological assessment as indicated. (12)

2. Help the patient see the relationship between medical problems and substance abuse.

RP: _____

_____

3. Teach the patient the medical issues surrounding substance abuse and explain that these illnesses pose a serious risk to health.

RP: _____

_____

4. Help the patient understand his/her medical problem and the need to cooperate with medical management.

RP: _____

_____

5. Help the patient develop a list of ten negative consequences that occurred as a result of using substance abuse to cope with medical problems.

RP: _____

_____

6. Physician will examine the patient and make recommendations as indicated to treat medical issues and alleviate symptoms.

RP: _____

_____

13. Implement relaxation exercises as a pain management technique. (15)

14. Accept and follow through on a referral to a pain management clinic. (16)

15. Discuss with family members the medical problems and substance abuse and make plans for recovery. (13)

16. List five ways a higher power can assist in recovery from medical problems and substance abuse. (14, 15)

17. Pray and meditate each day, asking for God's will and the power to carry it out. (14, 15)

18. Write a personal recovery plan that includes regular attendance at recovery groups and any medical treatment necessary to control medical issues and substance abuse. (16)

__. _____
   _____

__. _____
   _____

__. _____
   _____

7. Medical staff will monitor treatment plans as ordered by physician and will follow patient as needed.

   RP: _____

   _____

8. Educate the patient on the negative impact of substance abuse on bodily functioning and systems.

   RP: _____

   _____

9. Physician will teach the patient about the medical issues and substance abuse and will discuss treatment plans and follow-up.

   RP: _____

   _____

10. Medical staff will examine the patient for biomedical problems, develop a treatment plan, and monitor as necessary.

    RP: _____

    _____

11. Help the patient understand the importance of medical management and follow-up in aftercare.

    RP: _____

    _____

12. After discussion with the medical staff, help the patient list ten things

he/she can do to improve physical functioning (e.g., take medications; maintain abstinence, relaxation, proper diet, rest, and exercise; schedule follow-up visits with the physician).

RP: _____

_____

13. Psychologist will complete a psychological assessment as indicated and make recommendations for treatment.

RP: _____

_____

14. In a family session, discuss the medical issues and substance abuse and make plans for recovery (Alanon, Alateen, etc.).

RP: _____

_____

15. Teach relaxation and guided positive imagery as pain-coping skills.

RP: _____

_____

16. Refer patient to a pain clinic for medical and psychological management of pain.

RP: _____

_____

17. Explain the AA concept of a higher power and help the patient see how the higher power can be helpful in recovery.

    RP: _____

    _____

18. Explain step eleven and teach the patient how to use this step daily in recovery.

    RP: _____

    _____

19. Help the patient develop a personal recovery plan that details what the patient is going to do in recovery to remain abstinent and treat biomedical issues (e.g., regularly attend recovery groups, have regular medical checkups, take medication as indicated, get a sponsor, attend aftercare, help others).

    RP: _____

    _____

__. _____

    _____

    RP: _____

    _____

__. _____

    _____

    RP: _____

    _____

—. _____

_____

RP: _____

_____

DIAGNOSTIC SUGGESTIONS

Axis I:

307.89	Pain Disorder Associated With Both Psychological Factors and (Axis III Disorder)
307.80	Pain Disorder Associated With Psychological Factors
300.7	Hypochondriasis
300.81	Somatization Disorder
316	Personality Traits Affecting (Axis III Disorder)
316	Maladaptive Health Behaviors Affecting (Axis III Disorder)
316	Psychological Symptoms Affecting (Axis III Disorder)
307.23	Tourette's Disorder
293.0	Delirium
290	Dementia
_____	_____
_____	_____

NARCISSISM

BEHAVIORAL DEFINITIONS

1. A grandiose sense of self-importance and self-worth.
2. Fantasies of unlimited power, success, intelligence, or beauty.
3. Believes that he or she is special and only other special people can appreciate him or her.
4. A powerful need to be recognized, admired, and adored.
5. Becomes angry and resentful when people do not immediately meet his/her wishes, wants, and needs.
6. Lacks empathy for others.
7. Unreasonable expectations of others in relationships with little concern for the other person.
8. Often envious of others or feels others are envious of them.
9. Brags about his or her achievements, exaggerated abilities, and body image.
10. Interpersonally manipulative and exploitive.

__. _____
    _____
    _____
__. _____
    _____
    _____
__. _____
    _____

LONG-TERM GOALS

1. Maintain a program of recovery free of substance abuse and the negative effects of narcissistic traits.
2. Develop a realistic sense of self without narcissistic grandiosity, exaggeration, or sense of entitlement.

3. Understand the relationship between narcissistic traits and sub-stance abuse.
4. Understand narcissistic traits and how the sense of omnipotence places the patient at high risk for relapse.
5. Learn how to help others in recovery.
6. Develop empathy for other people, particularly victims of his or her narcissism.
7. Learn and demonstrate healthy impulse-control skills.
8. Develop healthy interpersonal relationships and communication skills.

—. _____
  _____
  _____
—. _____
  _____
  _____
—. _____
  _____

SHORT-TERM OBJECTIVES

1. Verbalize the powerlessness and unmanageability that results from narcissistic traits and substance abuse. (1, 2)

2. Verbally identify several narcissistic traits and state how they contribute to substance abuse. (2, 3)

3. List specific instances in which narcissistic traits led to substance abuse and describe the negative consequences that resulted from it. (2, 3)

THERAPEUTIC INTERVENTIONS

1. Using an AA step one exercise, help the patient see that narcissistic traits and substance abuse lead to a state of powerlessness and unmanageability.

   RP:* _____

   _____

2. Assist the patient in identifying his/her narcissistic traits and explain how they can lead to substance abuse.

   RP: _____

   _____

---

*RP = Responsible Professional

4. Verbalize a commitment to honesty and humility as the basis for a program of recovery. (4, 5, 6)

5. Verbally explain how manipulating others leads to interpersonal frustration and loneliness. (5, 7, 8)

6. List ten lies told to exaggerate accomplishments and seek acceptance and recognition. (7, 8)

7. List several narcissistic strategies used to manipulate others in relationships. (8)

8. In group sessions, identify regularly with the vulnerable revelations of other group members by sharing similar experiences, feelings, and thoughts. (9, 12, 13)

9. Identify with the feelings of others whom he/she has hurt by sharing similar situations from his/her family-of-origin experience of pain. (9, 11)

10. Identify a pattern of narcissism (anxious, fearful thoughts followed by exaggerated thoughts of power and importance) and replace that pattern with confident but realistic self-talk. (10, 13)

11. Verbalize ways in which the family-of-origin dynamics led to a poor self-image and a sense of rejection and failure. (10, 11)

3. Help the patient identify ten occasions when narcissistic traits and substance abuse led to negative consequences.

RP: _____

_____

4. Teach the patient how the 12 steps of AA can assist in recovery from narcissistic traits and substance abuse.

RP: _____

_____

5. Teach the patient that honesty is essential for real intimacy and that lies lead to interpersonal frustration and loneliness.

RP: _____

_____

6. Explain why resolution of narcissistic traits—especially the tendency toward dishonesty and feeling superior and all-powerful—is essential in maintaining abstinence.

RP: _____

_____

7. Have the patient list ten common lies told to exaggerate accomplishments and bolster self-image. Then show why the self-defeating lies eventually led to the rejection from others that he/she feared.

RP: _____

_____

12. Acknowledge that low self-esteem and fear of failure or rejection is felt internally in spite of the external facade of braggadocio. (11, 12, 13)

13. List five ways a higher power can assist in recovery from narcissistic traits and substance abuse. (14, 15)

14. Verbalize a commitment to helping others as essential to recovery from narcissistic traits and substance abuse. (9, 13, 16)

15. Practice stopping, thinking, listening, and planning before acting impulsively and without regard for other's rights and feelings. (12, 17)

16. In group, individual, and family sessions, practice honesty and realistic humility in communication. (12, 13, 17, 18)

17. In a family session, discuss narcissistic traits and substance abuse and help develop a program of recovery for each family member. (19)

18. Write a personal recovery plan that includes regular attendance at recovery groups and further treatment needed to recover from narcissistic traits and substance abuse. (20)

__. _____

_____

8. Help the patient list ten ways he/she uses narcissistic traits to control and manipulate others. Then explain how narcissistic behaviors are counterproductive to interpersonal acceptance and respect.

RP: _____

_____

9. Conduct group therapy sessions that focus on developing empathy by asking the patient to share with the group members his/her similar vulnerable, anxious experiences, feelings, and thoughts.

RP: _____

_____

10. Probe the patient's narcissistic thoughts (e.g., grandiosity, the sense of entitlement, the tendency to blame others, the need to exaggerate achievements in search of acceptance). Show the patient how these thoughts are based on low self-esteem and an expectation of rejection; then replace this pattern with confident, realistic self-talk.

RP: _____

_____

11. Probe the patient's family of origin for experiences of criticism, emotional abandonment or rejection, and abuse or neglect that led to

__. _____

_____

__. _____

_____

feelings of low self-esteem and narcissism.

RP: _____

_____

12. Confront expressions of entitlement and braggadocio, interpreting them as a cover for feelings of fear and low self-esteem.

    RP: _____

    _____

13. Reinforce social interactions that are characterized by humility, empathy, honesty, and compassion.

    RP: _____

    _____

14. Explain the AA concept of a higher power and teach the patient how this can be used in recovery.

    RP: _____

    _____

15. Using an AA step three exercise, teach the patient how to turn over problems to the higher power.

    RP: _____

    _____

16. Teach the patient that helping others will give him/her a genuine sense of self-worth, which is essential to working on a good program of recovery.

    RP: _____

    _____

17. Using modeling, role playing, and behavior rehearsal,
teach the patient the
impulse-control skills of
stopping, thinking, and
planning before acting.

RP: _____

_____

18. Use modeling, role playing,
and behavior rehearsal to
teach the patient healthy
interpersonal communica-
tion skills (e.g., be honest,
ask for what you want,
share how you feel, care
about what the other per-
son wants, listen actively,
and use "I messages").

RP: _____

_____

19. In a family session, teach
family members about
narcissistic traits and substance abuse and help each
family member develop
his/her own personal recovery plan.

RP: _____

_____

20. Help the patient develop a
personal recovery plan that
will detail what he/she is
going to do for further treatment in recovery (e.g., regularly attend recovery groups,
get a sponsor, seek further
treatment or therapy).

RP: _____

_____

___.   _____

        _____

    RP: _____

        _____

___.   _____

        _____

    RP: _____

        _____

___.   _____

        _____

    RP: _____

        _____

DIAGNOSTIC SUGGESTIONS

Axis I:	296.xx	Bipolar I Disorder
	296.89	Bipolar II Disorder
	301.13	Cyclothymic Disorder
	310.1	Personality Change Due to (Axis III Disorder)
	_____	_____
	_____	_____
Axis II:	301.81	Narcissistic Personality Disorder
	301.83	Borderline Personality Disorder
	301.50	Histrionic Personality Disorder
	301.4	Obsessive-Compulsive Personality Disorder
	_____	_____
	_____	_____

OCCUPATIONAL PROBLEMS

BEHAVIORAL DEFINITIONS

1. Feelings of inadequacy, fear, and failure secondary to severe business losses.
2. Rebellion against and/or conflicts with authority figures in the employment situation.
3. Underemployed or unemployed due to the negative effect of substance abuse on work performance and attendance.
4. Work environment is too stressful, leading to substance abuse to self-medicate.
5. Coworkers are alcohol/drug abusers and supportive of addiction, increasing the risk for patient's relapse.
6. Job jeopardy due to substance abuse.
7. Employer does not understand addiction or what is required for recovery.
8. Retirement has led to feelings of loneliness, lack of meaning to life, and substance abuse.
9. Anxiety related to perceived or actual job jeopardy.

___. _____
_____
___. _____
_____
___. _____
_____

LONG-TERM GOALS

1. Maintain a program of recovery free of substance abuse and occupational problems.

2. Educate work environment to be supportive of recovery.
3. Make plans to change occupation in order to maximize chances of recovery.
4. Understand the relationship between the stress of occupational problems and substance abuse.
5. Communicate with coworkers and management to obtain support for treatment and recovery.
6. Make a contract with management that details the recovery plan and consequences of relapse.
7. Arrange for on-site drug and/or alcohol testing and monitoring of recovery.
8. Fill life with new interests so retirement or job change can be appreciated.
9. Engage in job-seeking behaviors consistently and with a reasonably positive attitude.
10. Increase job satisfaction and performance due to implementation of assertiveness and stress management strategies.
11. Increase job security as a result of more positive evaluation of performance by supervisor.

—. _____

_____

—. _____

_____

—. _____

_____

SHORT-TERM OBJECTIVES

1. Identify the occupational problems and explain how they relate to substance abuse. (1, 2, 6, 7)

2. Identify patient's role in the conflict with coworkers or supervisor. (3, 4, 5)

THERAPEUTIC INTERVENTIONS

1. Take a history of the patient's occupational problems and determine how they relate to substance abuse.

RP:*_____

_____

---

*RP = Responsible Professional

3. Identify behavioral changes patient could make in interaction to help resolve conflict with coworkers or supervisors. (3, 4, 5)

4. List five occasions in which substance abuse led to occupational problems. (6)

5. List five ways occupational problems led to substance abuse. (7)

6. Verbalize reasons that current employment increases the risk for relapse. (6, 7, 8)

7. Verbalize feelings of fear, anger, and helplessness associated with the vocational stress. (9)

8. Identify distorted cognitive messages associated with perception of job stress. (10, 11, 12)

9. Develop healthier, more realistic cognitive messages that promote harmony with others, self-acceptance, and self-confidence. (11, 12, 13)

10. Replace projection of responsibility for conflict, feelings, or behavior with acceptance of responsibility for behavior, feelings, and role in conflict. (3, 12)

11. Develop a written plan to resolve occupational problems and maximize chances for recovery in the workplace. (14, 15)

2. Explain how the occupational problems led to substance abuse.

    RP: _____

    _____

3. Confront projection of responsibility for patient's behavior and feelings onto others.

    RP: _____

    _____

4. Discuss possible patterns of interpersonal conflict that occur beyond the work setting.

    RP: _____

    _____

5. Probe family-of-origin history for causes of current interpersonal conflict patterns.

    RP: _____

    _____

6. Help the patient list five occasions in which substance abuse led to problems at work.

    RP: _____

    _____

7. Help the patient see how problems at work led to more substance use.

    RP: _____

    _____

12. Meet with employer to discuss occupational stress and gain support for treatment and recovery. (14, 15, 17, 18, 19)

13. Role-play the assertiveness skills necessary to be honest with coworkers about addiction and recovery. (17, 18, 24)

14. List the skills or changes that will help in coping with current occupation. (16, 17, 18, 19, 20)

15. List five ways working on a program of recovery will improve occupational problems. (17, 20, 22, 23)

16. Write plans for a job change that will be supportive to recovery. (21)

17. List five ways a higher power can assist in recovery from occupational problems and substance abuse. (22, 23)

18. At least once a day, turn over to God the stress of the occupational problems and the urge for substance abuse. (22, 23)

19. Honestly acknowledge the negative impact substance abuse has had on work performance. (6, 24)

20. Write a personal recovery plan that includes regular attendance at recovery group meetings and any treatment necessary to

8. Help the patient see why his/her current employment creates a high risk for relapse (coworkers' substance abuse, job dissatisfaction, supervisor conflict, work hours too long, absence from family due to travel, ethical conflicts, etc.).

   RP: _____

   _____

9. Probe and clarify emotions surrounding the vocational stress.

   RP: _____

   _____

10. Assess the cognitive messages and schema connected with vocational stress.

    RP: _____

    _____

11. Help the patient develop more realistic, healthy cognitive messages that relieve anxiety and depression.

    RP: _____

    _____

12. Reinforce acceptance of responsibility for personal feelings and behavior.

    RP: _____

    _____

recover from substance abuse and occupational problems. (20, 25)

21. Discuss the grief over retirement and write plans to replace substance abuse with specific constructive activities. (26)

___. _____
_____

___. _____
_____

___. _____
_____

13. Confront the patient's catastrophizing the situation, which leads to immobilizing anxiety.

RP: _____
_____

14. Help the patient write a plan to resolve occupational problems and maximize recovery (e.g., regularly attend recovery groups, have regular drug testing, let management monitor recovery plan, be honest with management and coworkers).

RP: _____
_____

15. Meet with the patient and his/her employer to educate supervisor about addiction and to gain support for treatment and recovery.

RP: _____
_____

16. Using modeling, role playing, and behavior rehearsal, have the patient practice telling coworkers the truth about his/her substance abuse and plans for recovery.

RP: _____
_____

17. Help the patient learn the skills necessary to remain abstinent in his/her current work environment (e.g., be

honest with management and coworkers, attend regular recovery group meetings, use a sponsor, elicit the support of management, continue treatment).

RP: _____

_____

18. Use role playing, behavior rehearsal, and modeling to teach assertiveness skills.

RP: _____

_____

19. Help the patient develop the skills to reduce job stress and improve employment satisfaction (e.g., use time management skills, relaxation, and exercise; reduce responsibilities, work hours and travel time; have realistic expectations of work performance).

RP: _____

_____

20. Teach the patient how working on a 12-step program will improve occupational problems.

RP: _____

_____

21. Help the patient accept the need to change jobs to one that will be more supportive to recovery.

RP: _____

_____

22. Explain the AA concept of
   a higher power and discuss
   how this can assist in
   recovery.

   RP: _____

   _____

23. Using an AA step three
   exercise, teach the patient
   how to turn problems over
   to the higher power; then
   assign him/her to practice
   turning problems over to
   God at least once a day.

   RP: _____

   _____

24. Help the patient to be honest with self, coworkers,
   and management about
   substance abuse and its
   negative impact on job performance.

   RP: _____

   _____

25. Help the patient develop a
   personal recovery plan and
   review this plan with the
   employer.

   RP: _____

   _____

26. Help the patient work
   through the grief of retirement and then make plans
   to engage in constructive
   activities (volunteering,
   hobbies, exercise, social contacts, special-interest
   groups, AA meetings, con-

tinuing education, religious
involvement, etc.).

RP: _____

_____

__. _____

_____

RP: _____

_____

__. _____

_____

RP: _____

_____

__. _____

_____

RP: _____

_____

DIAGNOSTIC SUGGESTIONS

Axis I: V62.81   Relational Problem NOS
              V62.2   Occupational Problem
              V62.89   Phase of Life Problem
              300.02   Generalized Anxiety Disorder
              311   Depressive Disorder NOS
              296.xx   Major Depressive Disorder

              _____   _____

              _____   _____

Axis II: 301.7   Antisocial Personality Disorder
              301.0   Paranoid Personality Disorder

              _____   _____

              _____   _____

PARTNER RELATIONAL CONFLICTS

BEHAVIORAL DEFINITIONS

1. Relationship stress that provides an excuse for substance abuse and substance abuse that exacerbates the relationship conflicts.
2. Lack of communication with spouse or significant other.
3. Marital separation due to substance abuse.
4. Pending divorce.
5. A pattern of superficial or lack of communication, frequent arguing, infrequent sexual enjoyment, and a feeling of emotional distance from partner.
6. A pattern of substance use leading to social isolation and withdrawal.
7. A pattern of verbal or physical abuse present in the relationship.
8. Involvement in multiple superficial relationships, often with sexual intercourse, but without commitment or meaningful intimacy.
9. Inability to establish and maintain meaningful, intimate, interpersonal relationships.

—. _____
   _____
   _____
—. _____
   _____
   _____
—. _____
   _____

LONG-TERM GOALS

1. Maintain a program of recovery free of substance abuse and partner relational conflicts.

2. Terminate substance abuse and resolve the relationship conflicts that increase the risk of relapse.
3. Understand the relationship between substance abuse and partner relational conflicts.
4. Accept termination of the relationship and make plans to move forward in life.
5. Learn and demonstrate healthy communication skills.
6. Decrease partner relational conflict and increase mutually supportive interaction.
7. Encourage the partner to seek treatment for substance abuse.
8. Develop the ability to deal with partner relational conflict in a mature, controlled manner.
9. Develop the skills necessary to maintain open, effective communication, sexual intimacy, and enjoyable time together.
10. Decrease negative interaction and increase pleasurable activities together.

—. _____
_____
—. _____
_____
—. _____
_____

SHORT-TERM OBJECTIVES

THERAPEUTIC INTERVENTIONS

1. Verbalize the powerlessness and unmanageability that results from partner relational conflicts and substance abuse. (1, 2)

2. List five occasions in which substance abuse led to partner relational conflicts. (2, 3, 6)

1. Using an AA step one exercise, help the patient see that partner relational conflicts and substance abuse lead to powerlessness and unmanageability.

RP:*_____

_____

---

*RP = Responsible Professional

3. List five occasions in which relationship conflicts led to substance abuse. (2, 4, 6)

4. Verbalize acceptance of the responsibility for his/her role in relationship problems and in choosing substance abuse as a means of coping with the relationship conflicts. (3, 6)

5. Meet with the significant other or spouse to listen to and accept his/her perspective on the causes for the relational conflicts. (5, 6, 7)

6. Identify the positive and negative aspects of the current relationship. (6, 7)

7. Identify the causes for past and present conflicts within the relationship. (6, 7, 8)

8. List the changes that he/she believes each partner must make to restore the relationship. (6, 7, 8, 9)

9. Spouse or significant other to list the changes that he/she believes each partner must make to restore the relationship. (6, 10)

10. Develop a plan for each partner to change behaviors to improve the relationship. (9, 10, 11)

11. Discuss the sexual problems that exist in the relationship and demonstrate the ability to show intimacy verbally and nonverbally. (12, 13)

2. Help the patient understand how substance abuse has caused relationship conflicts and how relationship conflicts have precipitated substance abuse.

   RP: _____

   _____

3. Ask the patient to list five instances in which substance abuse led to relationship conflict.

   RP: _____

   _____

4. Ask the patient to list five occasions in which relationship conflicts led to substance abuse.

   RP: _____

   _____

5. Help the patient accept the responsibility for his/her role in the relationship problems and for choosing substance abuse as a reaction to the conflicts.

   RP: _____

   _____

6. In a conjoint session, take a history of the partner relational conflicts.

   RP: _____

   _____

12. Learn and demonstrate healthy communication skills. (14, 16, 17)

13. Accept the need for continued therapy to improve relationship and maintain gains. (15)

14. Write a plan to increase the quality and frequency of healthy communication with the partner. (14, 16, 17)

15. Grieve the loss of the relationship and make plans to move forward in life. (18, 19)

16. Write plans to increase pleasurable activities spent with the spouse or significant other. (20, 21)

17. Write a letter to the spouse or significant other sharing how the patient feels and asking for what he/she wants in recovery. (21)

18. Write a plan for meeting social and emotional needs during separation and divorce. (18, 19, 22)

19. Develop a personal recovery plan (e.g., regularly attend recovery groups, a sponsor, and seek any other therapy necessary to recover from partner relational conflicts and substance abuse). (15, 22)

20. Encourage the significant other or spouse to work on his/her own program of recovery. (23)

7. Ask the patient to list the positive and negative aspects of the relationship.

RP: _____

_____

8. Assist the patient in identifying the causes for past and present conflicts.

RP: _____

_____

9. Assign the patient the task of listing the behavioral changes he/she needs to make and the changes he/she believes the spouse or significant other needs to make to restore the relationship.

RP: _____

_____

10. Assign the spouse or significant other the task of listing the behavioral changes he/she needs to make and the changes he/she believes the partner needs to make to restore the relationship.

RP: _____

_____

11. In a conjoint session, obtain a commitment from each partner regarding which behaviors each will attempt to change.

RP: _____

_____

___. _____
        _____
___. _____
        _____
___. _____
        _____

12. In a conjoint session, facilitate a discussion of the sexual problems and make plans to improve intimacy and communication.

RP: _____

_____

13. Using modeling, role playing, and behavioral rehearsal, teach the partners how to show verbal and nonverbal affection to each other (e.g., going for a walk together, talking intimately, holding hands, hugging, dancing, giving each other compliments and praise).

RP: _____

_____

14. Using modeling, role playing, and behavioral rehearsal, teach the patient healthy communication skills (e.g., active listening, reflecting, sharing feelings, using "I messages").

RP: _____

_____

15. Help the couple see the importance of continued therapy to improve the relationship and maintain gains.

RP: _____

_____

16. Have the patient write a plan defining the time, place, and amount of time that will be devoted to private, one-to-one communication with partner each day.

RP: _____

_____

17. Facilitate a conjoint session that focuses on improving communication skills.

RP: _____

_____

18. Encourage the patient to share the grief of losing the significant other or spouse and help him/her write a plan to increase social interaction and improve old relationships.

RP: _____

_____

19. Encourage and support building new social relationships.

RP: _____

_____

20. Help the couple make a list of the pleasurable activities that they would like to do together; then help them make plans to become involved in one activity each week.

RP: _____

_____

21. Have the patient write a
letter to the partner sharing
how he/she feels and sug-
gesting pleasurable activities they could engage in
together during recovery.

RP: _____

_____

22. Help the patient develop a
written personal recovery
plan (e.g., regularly attend
recovery group meetings,
get a sponsor, and seek any
other therapy necessary to
recover from partner relational problems and sub-
stance abuse.

RP: _____

_____

23. Teach the patient and the
significant other or spouse
about 12-step recovery
groups (Alanon, Narcanon,
etc.)

RP: _____

_____

__. _____

_____

RP: _____

_____

__. _____

_____

RP: _____

_____

—. _____

_____

RP: _____

_____

DIAGNOSTIC SUGGESTIONS

Axis I: V61.1   Partner Relational Problem
              V62.81   Relational Problem NOS
              V61.1   Physical Abuse of Adult
              V61.1   Sexual Abuse of Adult

              _____   _____

Axis II: 301.7   Antisocial Personality Disorder
              301.20   Schizoid Personality Disorder
              301.81   Narcissistic Personality Disorder

              _____   _____
              _____   _____

PEER GROUP NEGATIVITY

BEHAVIORAL DEFINITIONS

1. Many friends and relatives are chemically dependent and encourage the patient to join them in substance abuse.
2. Peers are involved in the sale of illegal substances and encourage the patient to join them.
3. Peer group is not supportive of recovery from substance abuse.
4. Patient is involved in a gang that is supportive of criminal activity and substance abuse.
5. Peers do not understand addiction or the need for recovery.
6. Peers laugh and joke about recovery and continue to abuse substances.

—. _____
   _____
—. _____
   _____
—. _____
   _____

LONG-TERM GOALS

1. Maintain a program of recovery free of substance abuse and the negative influence of peers.
2. Understand that continuing to associate with the current peer group increases the risk for relapse.
3. Develop a new peer group that is drug free and supportive of working a program of recovery.

4. Attend recovery group meetings regularly and help others who are addicted.
5. Educate family members about addiction and the need for recovery.
6. Encourage family members who are addicted to seek treatment.
7. Learn the skills necessary to make new friends who are not substance abusers.

__. _____
   _____
   _____
__. _____
   _____
   _____
__. _____
   _____

SHORT-TERM OBJECTIVES

1. Verbalize the powerlessness and unmanageability that results from peer group negativity and substance abuse. (1, 2, 3, 4)

2. Identify several occasions when peer group negativity led to substance abuse. (2, 3, 4)

3. Verbalize an acceptance of the need for breaking ties with the current peer group. (2, 3, 4)

4. Verbalize how peer group negativity and substance abuse meets the AA concept of insanity. (2, 5)

THERAPEUTIC INTERVENTIONS

1. Using an AA step one exercise, help the patient see the powerlessness and unmanageability that result from peer group negativity and substance abuse.

   RP:*_____

   _____

2. Help the patient see the relationship between his/her peer group and substance abuse—particularly how the peer group often encouraged the use of alcohol/drugs.

   RP: _____

   _____

*RP = Responsible Professional

5. Accept AA step two by verbalizing how a higher power can restore the patient to sanity. (5, 6)

6. List five occasions in which peer group negativity led to criminal activity and substance abuse. (2, 3, 7)

7. List ten reasons the peer group has to be changed to maintain abstinence. (4, 8)

8. Verbalize the grief over the loss of the peer group and make plans for meeting new people in recovery. (4, 9)

9. List five ways a higher power can assist in recovery from peer group negativity and substance abuse. (4, 6, 9)

10. Verbalize reasons that obeying the law is essential for working on a program of recovery. (7, 10)

11. Turn one problem over to the higher power each day. Keep a journal of this behavior and discuss with primary therapist. (6, 11)

12. Write a plan describing how he/she will increase social interaction with a new peer group that is supportive of recovery. (12, 13)

13. Attend regular recovery group meetings and stay for coffee and conversation after each meeting. (12, 13)

3. Have the patient list instances in which peers encouraged substance abuse.

RP: _____

_____

4. Reinforce the patient's verbalized intent to break ties with the current peer group and empathize with the difficulty in leaving old friends and making new friends.

RP: _____

_____

5. Using an AA step two exercise, help the patient see how peer group negativity and substance abuse meets the AA concept of insanity.

RP: _____

_____

6. Explain the AA concept of a higher power and teach the patient how this power can restore sanity.

RP: _____

_____

7. Have the patient list five occasions in which the peer group lead him/her into criminal activity and substance abuse.

RP: _____

_____

14. Write an autobiography detailing the exact nature of the wrongs committed and relate these to the negative peer group and substance abuse. (14)

15. Practice drug refusal exercises in high-risk situations. (15)

16. Meet with a temporary sponsor and make plans to attend recovery group meetings. (12, 13, 16)

17. Meet with family members and discuss peer group negativity and substance abuse; then help make plans for recovery for each family member. (17)

___. _____
    _____

___. _____
    _____

___. _____
    _____

8. Help the patient see that continuing to associate with the current peer group increases the risk for relapse.

    RP: _____

    _____

9. Help the patient grieve the loss of the old peer group and make plans to develop new friends in recovery.

    RP: _____

    _____

10. Explain the AA concept of rigorous honesty and discuss why obeying the law is essential in working on a program of recovery.

    RP: _____

    _____

11. Using an AA step three exercise, teach the patient to turn over problems to the higher power each day; then assign him/her to use this step at least once a day. Have the patient keep a record of using step three and discuss how it worked.

    RP: _____

    _____

12. Have the patient write a plan describing how he/she plans to increase social contact with a new peer group that is positive toward recovery.

    RP: _____

    _____

13. Encourage the patient to stay for coffee and conversation after each AA/NA meeting to increase social skills and make new, positive friends.

    RP: _____

    _____

14. Using an AA step four inventory, assign the patient to write an autobiography detailing the exact nature of his/her wrongs and the relationship of these wrongs to the negative peer group and substance abuse.

    RP: _____

    _____

15. Using modeling, role playing, and behavioral rehearsal, teach the patient how to refuse alcohol/drugs; then practice refusal in the high-risk situations (e.g., in times of negative emotions, social pressure, interpersonal conflict, positive emotions, testing personal control).

    RP: _____

    _____

16. Introduce the patient to his/her AA/NA temporary sponsor and discuss plans for recovery.

    RP: _____

    _____

17. In a family session, teach the family members about peer group negativity and substance abuse and then help each family member develop a personal plan for recovery.

RP: _____

_____

__. _____

_____

RP: _____

_____

__. _____

_____

RP: _____

_____

__. _____

_____

RP: _____

_____

DIAGNOSTIC SUGGESTIONS

Axis I:	312.82	Conduct Disorder, Adolescent Onset Type
	309.4	Adjustment Disorder With Mixed Disturbance of Emotions and Conduct
	309.3	Adjustment Disorder With Disturbance of Conduct
	V62.81	Relational Problem NOS
	V71.01	Adult Antisocial Behavior
	V71.02	Child or Adolescent Antisocial Behavior
	_____	_____
	_____	_____

Axis II: 301.7   Antisocial Personality Disorder
301.83   Borderline Personality Disorder
301.81   Narcissistic Personality Disorder
301.82   Avoidant Personality Disorder

_____   _____

_____   _____

POSTTRAUMATIC STRESS

BEHAVIORAL DEFINITIONS

1. Past experience with a traumatic event that involved actual or threatened death or serious injury and caused a reaction of intense fear or helplessness.
2. Recurrent intrusive memories or dreams of the event.
3. Acting or feeling as if the trauma were recurring.
4. Intense distress when exposed to stimuli that prompt memories of the trauma.
5. Avoidance of stimuli that trigger traumatic memories.
6. Psychic numbing to avoid feelings or thoughts of the trauma.
7. Periods of disassociation or inability to remember parts of the trauma.
8. Persistent symptoms of increased autonomic arousal (e.g., difficulty sleeping, irritability, angry outbursts, difficulty concentrating, hypervigilance, or exaggerated startle response).

—. _____
   _____
   _____
—. _____
   _____
   _____
—. _____
   _____

LONG-TERM GOALS

1. Maintain a program of recovery free of substance abuse and post-traumatic stress.
2. Resolve the emotional effects of the past trauma and terminate the negative impact on current behavior.

3. Understand the relationship between posttraumatic stress and substance abuse.

4. Learn the coping skills necessary to bring posttraumatic stress and substance abuse under control.

5. Agree to attend the continuing care program necessary to effectively treat posttraumatic stress and substance abuse.

6. Understand posttraumatic stress symptoms and how they led to substance abuse in a self-defeating attempt to cope.

—. _____
   _____
—. _____
   _____
—. _____
   _____

SHORT-TERM OBJECTIVES

1. Verbalize the powerlessness and unmanageability that result from posttraumatic stress and substance abuse. (1)

2. Describe the traumatic events and the resultant feelings and thoughts in the past and present. (2)

3. List the times that posttraumatic stress symptoms led to substance abuse. (3)

4. List ways working a 12-step program of recovery can assist in recovery from posttraumatic stress and substance abuse. (4)

THERAPEUTIC INTERVENTIONS

1. Using an AA step one exercise, help the patient see that posttraumatic stress and substance abuse lead to powerlessness and unmanageability.

   RP:* _____
   _____

2. Explore the past traumatic event(s) and the associated feelings and thoughts.

   RP: _____
   _____

3. Have the patient list the occasions in which symp-

_____

*RP = Responsible Professional

5. List the feelings that led to disassociation. (2, 5)

6. Visit the physician to see if psychopharmacological intervention is warranted; then take all medications as directed. (6, 7)

7. Verbalize five ways a higher power can assist in recovery from posttraumatic stress and substance abuse. (8)

8. Turn posttraumatic stress and substance abuse over to God each day. Log this behavior and discuss with primary therapist. (8, 9)

9. Practice relaxation skills twice a day for at least 10 to 20 minutes. (10)

10. Cooperate in systematic desensitization sessions using imagery of the past trauma and current triggers for anxiety. (11)

11. Identify negative self-talk and catastrophizing that is associated with past trauma and current stimulus triggers for anxiety. (2, 12)

12. Approach actual stimuli (in vivo) that trigger memories and feelings associated with past trauma. Stay calm by using relaxation techniques and positive self-talk. (10, 11, 12, 13)

13. Practice turning perpetrators of painful trauma over to God. (8, 9, 14)

toms of posttraumatic stress led to substance abuse.

RP: _____

_____

4. Explain the 12 steps of AA/NA and discuss how they can assist in recovery.

RP: _____

_____

5. Help the patient uncover the feelings surrounding the past traumatic event and that lead to dissociation.

RP: _____

_____

6. Physician will examine the patient, order medications as indicated, titrate medications, and monitor for side effects and effectiveness.

RP: _____

_____

7. Medical staff will administer medications as ordered by the physician and monitor for side effects and effectiveness.

RP: _____

_____

8. Explain the AA concept of a higher power and discuss how this can be used in recovery.

RP: _____

_____

14. Sleep without being disturbed by dreams of the trauma. (10, 15, 18)

15. Express anger without rage, aggressiveness, or intimidation. (16, 17)

16. Practice stress management skills to reduce overall stress levels and craving. (10, 12, 18)

17. Develop a written personal recovery plan that details the steps to follow to maintain abstinence and recover from posttraumatic stress. (18, 19)

18. Verbalize five reasons that working on a program of recovery is essential to recover from posttraumatic stress and substance abuse. (19)

__. _____
   _____

__. _____
   _____

__. _____
   _____

9. Using an AA step three exercise, teach the patient how to turn problems over to God. Have the patient keep a record of this and then discuss how he/she felt using the step.
   RP: _____
   _____

10. Using progressive relaxation, biofeedback, or hypnosis, teach the patient how to relax; then assign him/her to relax twice a day for 10 to 20 minutes.
    RP: _____
    _____

11. Using systematic desensitization, have the patient experience avoidance situations, in imagery, of past trauma and current triggers for anxiety.
    RP: _____
    _____

12. Explore the negative self-talk that is associated with the past trauma and the predictions of unsuccessful coping or catastrophizing.
    RP: _____
    _____

13. Encourage the patient to approach previously avoided stimuli that trigger thoughts and feelings associated with the past trauma. Urge use of relaxation, deep breathing, and positive self-talk.
    RP: _____
    _____

14. Encourage the patient to turn perpetrators of pain over to God.

    RP: _____

    _____

15. Monitor patient's sleep pattern and encourage use of relaxation and positive imagery as aids to sleep.

    RP: _____

    _____

16. Review triggers to angry outbursts and teach the negative consequences of loss of control.

    RP: _____

    _____

17. Use role playing and behavioral rehearsal to teach assertive, respectful expression of angry feelings.

    RP: _____

    _____

18. Teach the patient stress management skills (e.g., use relaxation exercises and physical exercise, talk about problems, go to meetings, get a sponsor) to reduce level of anxiety and increase a sense of mastery over the environment.

    RP: _____

    _____

19. Help the patient develop a personal recovery plan (e.g., regularly attend recovery

group meetings, get a sponsor, take medications as directed, follow up with visits
to the therapist or doctor).

RP: _____

_____

—. _____

_____

RP: _____

_____

—. _____

_____

RP: _____

_____

—. _____

_____

RP: _____

_____

DIAGNOSTIC SUGGESTIONS

Axis I:	309.81	Posttraumatic Stress Disorder
	300.14	Dissociative Identity Disorder
	300.6	Depersonalization Disorder
	300.15	Dissociative Disorder NOS
	309.xx	Adjustment Disorder
	V61.21	Physical Abuse of Child
	V61.1	Physical Abuse of Adult
	V61.21	Sexual Abuse of Child
	V61.1	Sexual Abuse of Adult
	308.3	Acute Stress Disorder
	_____	_____
	_____	_____
Axis II:	301.83	Borderline Personality Disorder
	301.9	Personality Disorder NOS
	_____	_____
	_____	_____

PSYCHOSIS

BEHAVIORAL DEFINITIONS

1. Bizarre content of thought (delusions of grandeur, persecution, reference, influence, control, somatic sensations, or infidelity).
2. Illogical form of thought/speech (loose association of ideas in speech, incoherence; illogical thinking; vague, abstract, or repetitive speech; neologisms, perseverations, clanging).
3. Perception disturbance (hallucinations, primarily auditory but occasionally visual or olfactory).
4. Disturbed affect (blunted, none, flattened, or inappropriate).
5. Lost sense of self (loss of ego boundaries, lack of identity, blatant confusion).
6. Volition diminished (inadequate interest, drive, or ability to follow a course of action to its logical conclusion; pronounced ambivalence or cessation of goal-directed activity).
7. Relationship withdrawal (withdrawal from involvement with external world and preoccupation with egocentric ideas and fantasies, alienation feelings).
8. Psychomotor abnormalities (marked decrease in reactivity to environment; various catatonic patterns such as stupor, rigidity, excitement, posturing, or negativism, unusual mannerisms, or grimacing).
9. Inability to adequately care for own physical needs, which is potentially harmful to self.
10. Less intensive types of treatment are unsafe or have been unsuccessful.

___. _____

_____

___. _____

_____

—. _____

  _____

LONG-TERM GOALS

1. Control or eliminate active psychotic symptoms such that supervised functioning is positive and medication is taken consistently.
2. Significantly reduce or eliminate hallucinations and/or delusions.
3. Eliminate acute, reactive, psychotic symptoms and return to normal functioning in affect, thinking, and relating.
4. Stabilize functioning adequate to allow treatment in outpatient
   setting.
5. Develop adaptive methods to cope with symptoms and seek treatment when necessary.

—. _____

  _____

  _____

—. _____

  _____

  _____

—. _____

  _____

SHORT-TERM OBJECTIVES

1. Accept and understand that
   distressing symptoms are
   due to a mental illness or
   substance abuse. (1, 2,
   3, 23)

2. Understand the necessity
   for taking antipsychotic
   medications and agree to
   cooperate with prescribed
   care. (3, 4, 5)

THERAPEUTIC INTERVENTIONS

1. Determine if psychosis is of
   a brief, reactive nature or
   chronic with prodromal and
   reactive elements.

   RP:* _____

   _____

2. Explore family history for
   serious mental illness.

   RP: _____

   _____

_____

*RP = Responsible Professional

3. Take antipsychotic medications consistently as ordered by physician. (5, 6)

4. Comply with physical examination to evaluate for brain tumors, dementia, or other contributing organic factors. (7)

5. Describe auditory and visual hallucinations to staff when requested. (8, 11)

6. Verbalize delusional thoughts regarding irrational fear of harm from others or other distortions of reality regarding powers or traits of self or others. (9, 10, 11)

7. Verbalize a trust of others that is contrary to earlier beliefs of persecution or plotting of harm to self. (9, 10, 11)

8. Demonstrate reduction in thought disturbance by reporting less frequent and less severe hallucinations. (10, 11, 12, 13, 14)

9. Verbalize a cessation of hallucinations. (10, 11, 12, 13, 14)

10. Describe body parts as being normal and functional. (10, 11)

11. Cessation of bizarre behaviors such as talking to self, laughing or crying inappropriately, posturing, facial grimaces, incoherent speech, blank staring. (10, 11, 12, 13)

3. Evaluate the severity of patient's disturbance of reality perception and frequency of intrusive irrational thoughts.

RP: _____

_____

4. Psychiatrist to evaluate patient to determine need for antipsychotic medications.

RP: _____

_____

5. Psychiatrist to prescribe medications and adjust dosage as necessary to increase effectiveness and reduce side effects.

RP: _____

_____

6. Staff to administer medications and monitor for compliance, effectiveness, and side effects.

RP: _____

_____

7. Physician to provide physical exam to evaluate for organic factors that may contribute to psychosis.

RP: _____

_____

8. Gently provide an alternative, reality-based percep-

12. Meet with therapist to discuss progress toward reality orientation, appropriate affect, organized thought, and improved relational skills. (14, 15, 16)

13. Begin to show limited social functioning by responding appropriately to friendly encounters. (17)

14. Initiate contact with staff and patients and report feeling comfortable (not threatened) by the interaction. (17, 18)

15. Engage in social interaction that is reality-based, coherent, characterized by appropriate affect, subject-focused, logical, and organized. (17, 18)

16. Tend to basic needs of dress, hygiene, feeding self, grooming, and toileting without constant direction from staff. (19, 20)

17. Verbalize or write a plan for constructive activities for the day, and follow through on implementation of the plan. (20, 21, 22)

18. Attend therapy group and share thoughts and feelings that are organized, logical, and appropriate. (23, 24, 25, 26, 27)

19. Attend therapy group and report feeling comfortable with social interaction. (23, 24, 25, 26, 27)

tion to the patient when hallucinations are described.

RP: _____

9. Ask patient to verbalize irrational beliefs and assess content.

RP: _____

10. Calmly and matter-of-factly confront delusional thoughts, offering a reality-based explanation without debating it.

RP: _____

11. Encourage focus on the reality of external world versus the patient's distorted perceptions and beliefs.

RP: _____

12. Reinforce patient for calmness and normal appearance, behavior, and speech.

RP: _____

13. Staff to reduce level of stress and stimulation in milieu by speaking calmly, keeping noise levels low, maintaining structure and routine that is predictable, and engaging patient in

20. Attend therapy group and demonstrate appropriate social skills (no interruption, logical sequence to remarks within group conversation, comprehension of abstract comments). (25, 26, 27)

21. Replacement of pacing and other agitation behaviors with calm, appropriate sitting and a relaxed demeanor. (28, 29)

22. Attend recreational therapy and follow rules of interaction while reporting feeling nonthreatened. (30, 31)

23. Attend occupational therapy group and participate with actions that show initiative, logic, follow-through, and abstract reasoning. (32)

24. Use various art media to express and identify feelings of alienation, fear, and isolation. Engage in art therapy group discussion to identify feelings, enhance reality focus, and increase social contact. (33, 34)

25. Sleep in a normal pattern of six to nine hours per night without agitation, fears, or disruption. (35)

26. Family to verbalize an understanding that bizarre behavior and irrational thoughts are due to mental illness. (36, 37, 38, 39)

simple tasks that distract him/her from internal focus.

RP: _____

_____

14. Demonstrate acceptance through calm, nurturing manner, consistent eye contact, and active listening.

RP: _____

_____

15. Conduct individual therapy session to assess patient's progress toward reduction of thought disturbance.

RP: _____

_____

16. Provide supportive therapy to alleviate fears and reduce feelings of alienation.

RP: _____

_____

17. Staff to engage the patient in social interaction and give feedback regarding appropriateness of social skills.

RP: _____

_____

18. Reinforce patient for initiating appropriate social interaction with patients or staff.

RP: _____

_____

27. Family to increase frequency of statements of positive support of patient to reduce chances of acute exacerbation of patient's psychotic episode. (36, 37, 38, 39)

28. Cooperate with psychological testing to evaluate severity of thought disturbance. (40)

29. Cooperate with neuropsychological testing to evaluate presence of organicity. (41)

30. Verbalize an understanding and acceptance of the need for a structured, supervised living situation after discharge from intensive treatment. (42)

31. Verbalize an awareness of symptoms that are indicative of decompensation and establish methods to contact staff, clinician, and/or family/significant other if symptoms increase in intensity. (43, 44, 45)

32. Verbalize an understanding of the need for current medications, the importance of compliance and correct dosage, and knowledge of side effects and benefits. (43, 44, 45)

33. Write a personal substance abuse recovery plan that includes consistently attending recovery meet-

19. Prompt patient to complete activities of daily living (ADLs) to promote caring for own basic needs.

    RP: _____

    _____

20. Reinforce patient's independent performance of activities of daily living.

    RP: _____

    _____

21. Assign patient task of daily preparing a list of planned activities.

    RP: _____

    _____

22. Reinforce patient for implementing a plan of daily activities.

    RP: _____

    _____

23. Staff to direct patient to attend group therapy; then ask for a report on the content of the group and his/her contribution.

    RP: _____

    _____

24. Therapist to lead group therapy and draw patient into interaction.

    RP: _____

    _____

ings, getting a sponsor, helping others in recovery, and medically managing the psychosis. (47, 48)

34. Agree to move into the continuing care setting that will be structured enough to control substance abuse and psychosis. (47, 48)

__. _____
   _____

__. _____
   _____

__. _____
   _____

25. Therapist to reinforce patient for logical, coherent participation in group process.

RP: _____

_____

26. Therapist to gently confront hallucinations or delusions, providing a reality-based interpretation.

RP: _____

_____

27. Group therapist to reinforce patient for calm acceptance of social interaction without patient becoming agitated, bizarre, or distrustful.

RP: _____

_____

28. Staff to gently confront agitation behavior and calmly reassure patient of his/her safety.

RP: _____

_____

29. Staff to reinforce patient for a more relaxed demeanor and sitting calmly and normally.

RP: _____

_____

30. Direct recreational therapy activities that are non-threatening and simple to master, and encourage a low level of social interaction.

    RP: _____

    _____

31. Reinforce patient for appropriate participation in recreational activity.

    RP: _____

    _____

32. Direct occupational therapy activity that diverts patient from internal cognitive focus and provides structured social interaction and a sense of accomplishment on the completion of a task.

    RP: _____

    _____

33. Conduct art therapy group in which the patient is encouraged to express feelings though various art media.

    RP: _____

    _____

34. Lead group discussion to share meaning of artwork.

    RP: _____

    _____

35. Staff to direct patient to sleep at expected times and reinforce compliance.

    RP: _____

    _____

36. Arrange therapy sessions to educate family regarding patient's illness, treatment, and prognosis.

    RP: _____

    _____

37. Encourage family members to share their feelings of frustration, guilt, fear, or grief surrounding patient's mental illness and behavior patterns.

    RP: _____

    _____

38. Help the family replace double-bind messages that are inconsistent and contra-dictory—resulting in increased anxiety, confusion, and psychotic symp-toms in the patient—with clear, direct, concrete communication.

    RP: _____

    _____

39. Hold family therapy sessions to reduce the atmosphere of criticism and hostility toward the patient and promote compassion, empathy, and support for patient.

    RP: _____

    _____

40. Perform psychological testing to evaluate the perva-
siveness of thought
disturbance.

    RP: _____

    _____

41. Perform neuropsychological
testing to evaluate for
organicity.

    RP: _____

    _____

42. Arrange for an appropriate
level of supervised, residential care for the patient.

    RP: _____

    _____

43. Assess the patient's ability
to follow through with the
skills learned in treatment.

    RP: _____

    _____

44. Educate the patient regarding critical symptoms that
are indicative of decompensation and urge initiation of
clinical contact if intense
positive symptoms of psy-
chosis appear and interfere
with daily functioning.

    RP: _____

    _____

45. Provide the patient with
written instructions and
phone numbers to use if
symptoms become intense.

    RP: _____

    _____

46. Educate the patient and/or family or significant other about the importance of medication compliance, proper dosage, refilling prescriptions, safety factors, and recognition of side effects.

    RP: _____

    _____

47. Help the patient develop a personal recovery plan (e.g., consistently attend recovery group meetings, get a sponsor, help others in recovery, and medically manage the psychosis).

    RP: _____

    _____

48. Discuss alternatives for continuing care treatment (halfway house, group home, therapeutic community, hospitalization, etc.) in the least restrictive setting necessary to control substance abuse and psychosis.

    RP: _____

    _____

—. _____

    _____

    RP: _____

    _____

___·   _____

_____

RP: _____

_____

___·   _____

_____

RP: _____

_____

DIAGNOSTIC SUGGESTIONS

Axis I: 291.x   Alcohol-Induced Psychotic Disorder
292.xx   Other (or Unknown) Substance-Induced
          Disorder
295.xx   Schizophrenia
296   Major Depressive Disorder
296.xx   Bipolar I Disorder
296.89   Bipolar II Disorder
297.1   Delusional Disorder
298.8   Brief Psychotic Disorder
295.40   Schizophreniform Disorder
295.70   Schizoaffective Disorder
310.1   Personality Change Due to (Axis III Disorder)

_____   _____

_____   _____

RELAPSE-PRONE

BEHAVIORAL DEFINITIONS

1. Patient has a history of multiple treatment attempts and relapse.
2. Negative emotions place the patient at high risk for continued substance abuse.
3. Friends or family members are substance abusers.
4. Interpersonal conflicts place the patient at high risk for relapse.
5. Social pressure encourages substance use.
6. Patient has never worked on a program of recovery long enough to maintain abstinence.
7. Mental illness places the patient at high risk for relapse.

___. _____
_____
___. _____
_____
___. _____
_____

LONG-TERM GOALS

1. Reduce the risk for relapse and maintain a program of recovery free of substance abuse.
2. Resolve interpersonal conflicts and learn healthy communication skills.
3. Develop a new peer group supportive of recovery.
4. Learn alcohol/drug refusal skills.
5. Develop coping skills to use when experiencing high-risk situations and/or craving.

6. Learn and practice a program of recovery (e.g., regularly attend recovery group meetings, work with a sponsor, and help others in recovery).

7. Understand and take all medications as ordered by the physician.

—. _____

_____

—. _____

_____

—. _____

_____

SHORT-TERM OBJECTIVES

1. Write a detailed chemical-use history describing treatment attempts and the specific situations surrounding relapse. (1, 2)

2. Verbalize an understanding of why the patient continues to relapse. (1, 2)

3. Verbalize the powerlessness and unmanageability that results from substance abuse and relapse. (2, 3, 4)

4. Verbalize an acceptance of powerlessness over alcohol/drugs. (2, 3, 4, 5)

5. Verbalize that continued alcohol/drug use meets the AA concept of insanity. (2, 3, 4, 5)

6. Verbalize five reasons why it is essential to work on a daily program of recovery

THERAPEUTIC INTERVENTIONS

1. Have the patient write a chemical-use history describing his/her attempts at recovery. Teach the patient the high-risk situations (e.g., negative emotions, social pressure, interpersonal conflict, positive emotions, testing personal control) that lead to relapse.

   RP:*_____

   _____

2. Help the patient understand the reasons for continued relapsing (e.g., failure to work on a daily program of recovery, failure to go to meetings, poor coping skills, mental illness, interpersonal problems, poor recovery environment).

   RP: _____

   _____

---

*RP = Responsible Professional

to maintain abstinence.
(2, 6, 7)

7. List five reasons for
patient's failure to work on
a daily program of recovery.
(2, 6, 7)

8. Turn problems over to God
each day, praying only for
His will and the power to
carry it out. Record each of
these events and discuss
with primary therapist.
(8, 9)

9. List five ways a higher
power can assist in recovery
from substance abuse.
(8, 9)

10. Verbalize reasons the
patient does not continue to
attend AA/NA meetings
long enough to maintain
abstinence. (7, 10)

11. Write a plan to increase
reinforcement when attending recovery group meet-
ings. (10, 11, 12)

12. Develop a new peer group
supportive of recovery.
(11, 12)

13. Develop a written plan to
deal with each high-risk
situation (e.g., negative
emotions, social pressure,
interpersonal conflict, positive emotions, testing
personal control).
(13, 14, 15, 16)

14. Practice healthy communication skills. (14, 15)

3. Using an AA step one exercise, help the patient see
the powerlessness and
unmanageability that result
from substance abuse and
relapse.

RP: _____

_____

4. Using the chemical-use history, help the patient accept
his/her powerlessness over
alcohol/drugs.

RP: _____

_____

5. Using an AA step two exercise, help the patient see
the insanity of his/her disease; then teach the patient
that a higher power can
restore him/her to sanity.

RP: _____

_____

6. Help the patient understand that working on a
daily program of recovery is
essential to maintain abstinence.

RP: _____

_____

7. Using a relapse history,
help the patient understand
the reasons he/she failed to
work on a program of recovery.

RP: _____

_____

15. Write a plan to resolve interpersonal conflicts. (14, 15)

16. Practice alcohol/drug refusal skills. (14, 15, 16)

17. Visit physician to see if pharmacological intervention is warranted, and take all medication as directed. (17, 18)

18. Make a card of emergency phone numbers to call for help in a high-risk situation. (19)

19. Agree to enter the structured continuing care treatment setting necessary to maintain abstinence. (20, 21)

20. Develop a written personal recovery plan (e.g., be honest, regularly attend recovery group meetings, get a sponsor, and seek any other treatment needed to maintain abstinence). (20, 21)

___. _____
    _____

___. _____
    _____

___. _____
    _____

8. Teach the patient how to use the AA step three and have him/her practice turning problems over to God each day. Have the patient record each situation and discuss with primary therapist.
   RP: _____

   _____

9. Teach the patient how the higher power can assist in recovery.
   RP: _____

   _____

10. Probe the reasons the patient discontinues going to AA/NA meetings.
    RP: _____

    _____

11. Help the patient develop a plan that will increase the rewards obtained at recovery groups (e.g., concentrate on helping others, go for dessert after the meeting, socialize, stick with the winners).
    RP: _____

    _____

12. Assign the patient an AA/NA contact person and begin to attend regular recovery group meetings with him/her. Encourage both individuals to make the outing fun rather than a boring obligation.
    RP: _____

    _____

13. Help the patient write a plan to carry at all times that details the coping skills to use in high-risk situations. For example, go to a meeting, call the sponsor, call the AA hot line, call the counselor/doctor or treatment center, or talk to someone about the problem.

RP: _____

_____

14. Teach the patient healthy communication skills (e.g., listen actively, use "I messages," reflect, share feelings).

RP: _____

_____

15. Teach the patient conflict resolution skills; use modeling, role playing, and behavior rehearsal to have him/her practice handling conflict in high-risk situations.

RP: _____

_____

16. Use modeling, role playing, and behavior rehearsal to teach the patient how to say no to alcohol/drugs; then practice refusal in several high-risk situations.

RP: _____

_____

17. Physician will examine the patient, order medications

as indicated, titrate medications, and monitor for side
effects.

RP: _____

_____

18. Medical staff will administer medications as ordered
by the physician and monitor for side effects.

RP: _____

_____

19. Help the patient make an
emergency card to carry at
all times that has the phone
numbers of people to call in
high-risk situations.

RP: _____

_____

20. Help the patient decide on
the aftercare placement
that is structured enough to
help him/her maintain
abstinence (e.g., halfway
house, group home, outpa-
tient treatment, day care,
partial hospitalization).

RP: _____

_____

21. Help the patient develop a
written continuing care
plan that includes the
essential elements neces-
sary for him/her to main-
tain abstinence and
continue recovery.

RP: _____

_____

—. _____

_____

RP: _____

_____

—. _____

_____

RP: _____

_____

—. _____

_____

RP: _____

_____

DIAGNOSTIC SUGGESTIONS

Axis I: 312.8   Conduct Disorder
              296.xx   Bipolar I Disorder
              296.89   Bipolar II Disorder
              301.13   Cyclothymic Disorder
              314   Attention-Deficit/Hyperactivity Disorder
              313.81   Oppositional Defiant Disorder

              _____   _____

Axis II: 301.0   Paranoid Personality Disorder
              301.20   Schizoid Personality Disorder
              301.22   Schizotypal Personality Disorder
              301.7   Antisocial Personality Disorder
              301.83   Borderline Personality Disorder
              301.81   Narcissistic Personality Disorder
              301.82   Avoidant Personality Disorder

              _____   _____

              _____   _____

SPIRITUAL CONFUSION

BEHAVIORAL DEFINITIONS

1. Confusion about spiritual matters leads to a negative attitude about recovery.
2. Holding religious convictions that identify alcoholism as a sin rather than as a disease leads to a negative attitude about a 12-step program of recovery.
3. Fearing that God is angry prevents patient from connecting with a higher power.
4. Anger at God prevents patient from consciously seeking contact with God.
5. Active involvement in a religious system that does not support a 12-step recovery program.
6. Need for a higher power is not understood.
7. Existence of a higher power is not supported by spiritual beliefs.

___. _____
_____
___. _____
_____
___. _____
_____

LONG-TERM GOALS

1. Make conscious contact with God using prayer and meditation.
2. Understand the relationship between spiritual confusion and substance abuse.
3. Accept that a higher power can assist in relieving the patient's substance abuse.

4. Develop a concept of a higher power that is loving and supportive to recovery.
5. Learn the difference between religion and spirituality.
6. Maintain a recovery program free of substance abuse and spiritual confusion.
7. Learn and demonstrate the 12-step concept of "God as we understand Him."
8. Develop and use a healthy concept of a higher power.

—. _____
   _____
   _____

—. _____
   _____
   _____

—. _____
   _____

SHORT-TERM OBJECTIVES

1. Verbalize the powerlessness and unmanageability that results from spiritual confusion and substance abuse. (1, 2, 3, 4, 5)

2. Verbally identify how spiritual confusion leads to substance abuse. (1, 2, 3, 4, 5)

3. Verbalize how spiritual confusion can lead to a condemning attitude toward substance abusers and resistance toward working a 12-step program of recovery. (1, 2, 3, 4, 5)

4. Verbalize an understanding of spiritual confusion and its relation to substance

THERAPEUTIC INTERVENTIONS

1. Using an AA step one exercise, help the patient accept that he/she is powerless over spiritual confusion and mood-altering chemicals and that his/her life is unmanageable.

   RP:*_____

   _____

2. Take a spiritual history to explore the patient's spiritual confusion and relate it to substance abuse and recovery.

   RP: _____

   _____

*RP = Responsible Professional

abuse and recovery.
(2, 3, 4, 5, 6)

5. List five instances when spiritual confusion led to substance abuse. (4, 5, 6)

6. Verbalize how substance abuse and spiritual confusion left the patient spiritually bankrupt. (2, 4, 5, 6)

7. Verbalize an understanding of the 12-step concept of "God as we understood Him." (7, 8, 9)

8. Verbalize how many different religions and cultures can work a 12-step recovery program. (8, 9)

9. Verbalize an understanding of God's grace and willingness to forgive. (8, 10, 11)

10. List ten ways a higher power can assist in recovery from spiritual confusion and substance abuse. (10, 11, 12, 13, 14)

11. Verbalize an understanding of page 449 in the *Big Book* (Alcoholics Anonymous 1976). (12)

12. Meet with a member of the clergy familiar with 12-step recovery and discuss the higher power and how it can assist in recovery. (13)

13. Meet with a temporary sponsor or AA/NA contact person, and discuss plans for resolving spiritual confusion and substance abuse. (14)

3. Help the patient understand how negative attitudes toward spiritual matters make recovery difficult.

RP: _____

_____

4. Probe the patient's spiritual confusion and explain how this confusion contributed to substance abuse and a negative attitude toward recovery.

RP: _____

_____

5. Help the patient understand the relation between spiritual confusion and substance abuse.

RP: _____

_____

6. Help the patient identify how substance abuse leads to spiritual confusion.

RP: _____

_____

7. Using an AA step two exercise, help the patient see the insanity of his/her spiritual confusion and substance abuse and help him/her see that a higher power can assist in relieving the disease.

RP: _____

_____

14. Verbalize the need to begin a spiritual journey outlined in the 12 steps. (13, 14, 15, 16)

15. Write a plan to continue a spiritual journey as outlined in the 12 steps. (13, 14, 15, 16)

16. Write a letter to God sharing the patient's feelings and asking for what he/she wants in recovery. (17)

17. Decide to turn the patient's will and life over to God as he/she understands Him. (18, 19)

18. Practice prayer and meditation at least once a day. (18, 19, 20)

19. Keep a prayer journal to write down all of the things the patient prays for and thinks God is saying. (18, 19, 20, 21)

20. Ask God to come into the patient's life each day; then ask: "God, what is the next step in my relationship with you." Write down each answer from God and share with the primary therapist. (18, 19, 20, 21)

21. Write a personal recovery plan that includes regular attendance at recovery groups, getting a sponsor, helping others in recovery, and any other treatment necessary to recover from spiritual confusion and substance abuse. (22)

8. Teach the patient about the 12-step concept of "God as we understood Him," and how this relates to the patient's spiritual confusion.

RP: _____

_____

9. Teach the patient how many different religions and cultures can work a similar 12-step recovery program.

RP: _____

_____

10. Teach the patient that God will forgive him/her for his/her wrongs.

RP: _____

_____

11. Teach the patient about the importance of a higher power in a 12-step program and show the patient how a higher power can assist in recovery.

RP: _____

_____

12. Have the patient read page 449 in the *Big Book;* then teach him/her how everything that happens in the world is a part of God's good plan.

RP: _____

_____

—. _____

_____

—. _____

_____

—. _____

_____

13. Arrange for the patient to meet a member of the clergy familiar with 12-step recovery and encourage the patient to share thoughts and feelings about the higher power.

RP: _____

_____

14. Arrange for the patient to meet with an AA contact person, or temporary sponsor, and discuss 12-step recovery, spiritual confusion, and substance abuse.

RP: _____

_____

15. Have the patient read "How it Works," in the *Big Book* and discuss the three pertinent ideas outlined at the end of the chapter: (a) "we were alcoholic and could not manage our own lives; (b) probably no human power could have relieved our alcoholism; and (c) God could and would if He were sought."

RP: _____

_____

16. Using the 12 steps as a guide, help the patient write a plan to continue his/her spiritual journey.

RP: _____

_____

17. Write a letter to God sharing how the patient thinks
and feels and asking for
what he/she wants in recovery.

RP: _____

_____

18. Using an AA step three
exercise, teach the patient
how to turn problems over
to God.

RP: _____

_____

19. Have the patient read chapter eleven in AA's *Twelve
Steps and Twelve Tradi-
tions,* teach the patient how
to pray (talk to God) and
meditate (listen for God),
then direct the patient to
pray and meditate at least
once each day.

RP: _____

_____

20. Keep a prayer journal for
writing down the patient's
prayers and any communi-
cation from God.

RP: _____

_____

21. Have the patient ask God to
come into his/her life each
day; then ask: "God, what is
the next step in my rela-
tionship with you." Have
the patient write down each
communication from God

and share it with primary
therapist.

RP: _____

_____

22. Help the patient develop a
personal recovery plan that
includes regular attendance
at recovery groups, getting
a sponsor, helping others in
recovery, and any other
treatment necessary to
recover from spiritual confusion and substance abuse.

RP: _____

_____

—. _____

_____

RP: _____

_____

—. _____

_____

RP: _____

_____

—. _____

_____

RP: _____

_____

DIAGNOSTIC SUGGESTIONS

Axis I: V62.89   Religious or Spiritual Problem
                 V62.4   Acculturation Problem

_____   _____

_____   _____

SUBSTANCE ABUSE/DEPENDENCE

BEHAVIORAL DEFINITIONS

1. Maladaptive pattern of substance use manifested by increased tolerance and withdrawal.
2. Inability to stop or cut down use of mood-altering drug despite the verbalized desire to do so and the negative consequences of continued use.
3. Blood work (elevated liver enzymes, electrolyte imbalance, etc.) and physical indicators (stomach pain, high blood pressure, malnutrition, etc.) reflect a pattern of heavy substance use.
4. Denial that chemical dependence is a problem despite feedback from significant others that the substance use is negatively affecting them.
5. Frequent blackouts when using.
6. Continued substance use despite persistent physical, legal, financial, vocational, social, or relationship problems that are directly caused by the substance use.
7. Drug tolerance increases as increased substance use is required to become intoxicated or to recall the desired effect.
8. Physical withdrawal symptoms (shaking, seizures, nausea, headaches, sweating, anxiety, insomnia, and/or depression) when going without the substance for any length of time.
9. Arrests for substance abuse–related offenses (e.g., driving under the influence, minor in possession, assault, possession/delivery of a controlled substance, shoplifting.).
10. Suspension of important social, recreational, or occupational activities because they interfere with using.
11. Large time investment in activities to obtain the substance, use it, or recover from its effects.
12. Consumption of substance in greater amounts and for longer periods than intended.

13. Continued use of mood-altering chemical despite physician's warning that using is causing health problems.

___. _____

_____

___. _____

_____

___. _____

_____

LONG-TERM GOALS

1. Accept powerlessness and unmanageability over mood-altering substances and participate in a recovery-based program.
2. Accept chemical dependence and begin to actively participate in a recovery program.
3. Establish a sustained recovery, free from the use of all mood-altering substances.
4. Establish and maintain total abstinence while increasing knowledge of the disease and the recovery process.
5. Acquire the necessary skills to maintain long-term sobriety from all mood-altering substances and live a life free of chemicals.
6. Improve quality of life by maintaining abstinence from all mood-altering chemicals.
7. Withdraw from mood-altering substance, stabilize physically and emotionally, and then establish a supportive recovery plan.

___. _____

_____

___. _____

_____

___. _____

_____

SHORT-TERM OBJECTIVES

1. Cooperate with medical assessment and an evaluation of the necessity for pharmacological intervention. (1, 2)

2. Take prescribed medications as directed by the physician. (2, 3)

3. Report acute withdrawal symptoms to the staff. (4)

4. Provide honest and complete information for a chemical dependence biopsychosocial history. (5)

5. Attend didactic sessions and read assigned material to increase knowledge of addiction and the process of recovery. (6, 7, 8, 9)

6. Attend group therapy sessions to share thoughts and feelings associated with, reasons for, consequences of, feelings about, and alternatives to substance abuse. (10, 11)

7. List ten negative consequences resulting from or exacerbated by substance dependence. (12, 13)

8. Verbally admit to powerlessness over mood-altering substances. (12, 13)

9. Verbalize an understanding of the problems caused by

THERAPEUTIC INTERVENTIONS

1. Physician will perform a physical exam and write treatment orders, including, if necessary, prescription of medications.

   RP:* _____

   _____

2. Physician will monitor the side effects and effectiveness of medication, titrating as necessary.

   RP: _____

   _____

3. Staff will administer prescribed medications and monitor for side effects and effectiveness.

   RP: _____

   _____

4. Staff will assess and monitor patient's condition during withdrawal using a standardized procedure (e.g., Clinical Institute of Withdrawal Scale) as needed.

   RP: _____

   _____

5. Complete a thorough family and personal biopsychosocial history focusing on substance abuse.

   RP: _____

   _____

_____

*RP = Responsible Professional

the use of mood-altering substances and, therefore, the need to stay in treatment. (12, 13)

10. Verbalize a recognition that mood-altering chemicals were used as the primary coping mechanism to escape from stress or pain, and their use resulted in negative consequences. (14, 15)

11. List the negative emotions that were caused or exacerbated by substance dependence. (14, 15)

12. List the social, emotional, and family factors that contributed to substance dependence. (5, 16)

13. List ten reasons to work on a substance abuse–recovery plan. (14, 15, 17)

14. List ten lies used to hide substance dependence. (18)

15. Verbalize five ways a higher power can assist in recovery. (19, 24)

16. Practice turning problems over to God each day. Record each event and share with primary therapist. (19, 24)

17. Practice healthy communication skills to reduce stress and increase positive social interaction. (20)

18. Practice problem-solving skills. (21)

6. Have the patient attend a chemical dependence didactic series to increase knowledge of the patterns and effects of chemical dependence.

RP: _____

_____

7. Require the patient to attend all chemical dependence didactics; ask him/her to identify several key points learned from each didactic, and process these points with the therapist.

RP: _____

_____

8. Ask the patient to read Ohm's pamphlet on marijuana or another specific cannabis-related article and process with the therapist five key points learned from the reading.

RP: _____

_____

9. Assign pages 1 to 164 in *Alcoholics Anonymous: The Big Book* and gather five key points from it to process with the therapist.

RP: _____

_____

10. Require patient's attendance at group therapy.

RP: _____

_____

19. List the reasons for substance use and adaptive alternatives. (22, 23, 25)

20. Verbalize options to substance use in dealing with stress and finding pleasure or excitement in life. (21, 22, 23, 24, 25)

21. Write a leisure-skills program to decrease stress and improve health. (25, 27)

22. Practice stress management skills to reduce overall stress levels, relax, and feel comfortable. (26, 27)

23. Exercise at a training heart rate (220 − age × .75 to .85) for at least 20 minutes at least three times per week. (27)

24. Complete a fourth-step inventory and share it with a member of the clergy or someone else in the program. (28)

25. List the triggers (persons, places, and things) that may precipitate relapse. (14, 22, 29)

26. Write a plan to cope with each high-risk or trigger situation. (29, 30, 31)

27. Practice saying no to alcohol and drugs. (31)

28. Write a personal recovery plan that includes regular attendance at recovery group meetings, aftercare, getting a sponsor, and helping others in recovery. (32, 33)

11. Direct group therapy that facilitates the sharing of, causes for, consequences of, feelings about, and alternatives to substance abuse.

RP: _____

_____

12. Have the patient complete an Alcoholics Anonymous (AA) first-step paper admitting to powerlessness over mood-altering chemicals, and present it in group therapy or to therapist for feedback.

RP: _____

_____

13. Ask the patient to list ways chemical use has negatively impacted his/her life and process the list with the therapist or group.

RP: _____

_____

14. Explore substance abuse as an escape from stress, physical and emotional pain, and boredom. Confront the negative consequences of this pattern of behavior.

RP: _____

_____

15. Probe the sense of shame, guilt, and low self-worth that has resulted from sub-

29. Take a personal inventory at the end of each day listing recovery problems, plans to address the problems, and five things for which the patient was grateful that day. (33, 34)

30. Enter the continuing care treatment setting necessary to maintain abstinence and maximize chances for recovery. (35)

31. Meet with family members and have them verbalize an understanding of their role in the disease and the recovery process. (36, 37, 38, 39, 40, 41)

32. Decrease the frequency with which family members enable the chemically dependent child after they verbally identify their enabling behaviors. (37, 38, 39, 40)

33. Help each family member develop a recovery program for the familial aspects of chemical dependence. (41, 42)

___. _____
   _____
___. _____
   _____
___. _____
   _____

stance abuse and its consequences.
RP: _____
_____

16. Use the biopsychosocial history to help the patient understand the familial, emotional, and social factors that contributed to the development of chemical dependence.
RP: _____
_____

17. Have the patient list ten reasons to abstain from substance use.
RP: _____
_____

18. Help the patient see the dishonesty that goes along with substance abuse. Have patient list ten lies he/she told to hide substance use. Then teach patient why honesty is essential to recovery.
RP: _____
_____

19. Explain the AA concept of a higher power and teach the patient how this can assist in recovery.
RP: _____
_____

20. Teach the patient healthy communication skills (e.g., using I messages, reflecting,

active listening, empathy, being reinforcing, sharing).

RP: _____

_____

21. Using modeling, role playing, and behavioral rehearsal, teach the patient how to solve problems in an organized fashion (e.g., write the problem, think accurately, list the options of action, evaluate alternatives, act, monitor results).

RP: _____

_____

22. Help the patient clarify why he/she was using substances and identify other ways to achieve the same results.

RP: _____

_____

23. Teach the patient how to enjoy life without using mood-altering substances.

RP: _____

_____

24. Using an AA step three exercise, teach the patient about the AA concept of "turning it over." Then have the patient turn problems over to the higher power each day and record these events for later discussion.

RP: _____

_____

25. Have the patient list the pleasurable activities he/she plans to use in recovery.

    RP: _____

    _____

26. Using progressive relaxation or biofeedback, teach the patient how to relax; then have him/her relax twice a day for 10 to 20 minutes.

    RP: _____

    _____

27. Using current physical fitness levels, help the patient exercise three times a week; then increase the exercise by 10 percent a week until he/she is exercising at a training heart rate ($220 - \text{age} \times .75$ to $.85$) for at least 20 minutes at least three times a week.

    RP: _____

    _____

28. Have the patient complete a fourth-step inventory, then make arrangements for him/her to share this with a member of the clergy or someone else in recovery.

    RP: _____

    _____

29. Using an AA relapse-prevention exercise, help the patient uncover his/her relapse triggers.

    RP: _____

    _____

30. Teach the patient about high-risk situations (e.g., negative emotions, social pressure, interpersonal conflict, positive emotions, and testing personal control). Help the patient write a plan to cope with each high-risk situation.

    RP: _____

    _____

31. Using modeling, role playing, and behavioral rehearsal, teach the patient how to say no to alcohol/drugs; then practice saying no in high-risk situations.

    RP: _____

    _____

32. Help the patient develop a personal recovery plan that includes regular attendance at recovery group meetings, aftercare, getting a sponsor, and helping others in recovery.

    RP: _____

    _____

33. Help the patient understand the necessity for working on a personalized recovery program every day to maintain abstinence.

    RP: _____

    _____

34. Encourage the patient to take a personal inventory each night, listing the prob-

lems he/she had that day,
making a plan to deal with
them, and then listing five
things he/she was grateful
for that day.

RP: _____

_____

35. Discuss continuing care
options with the patient
(regular meetings, therapy,
halfway house, group home,
therapeutic community,
etc.).

RP: _____

_____

36. Request the patient's family
attend Al-Anon, Nar-Anon,
or Tough Love meetings.

RP: _____

_____

37. Teach the patient's family
about the dynamics of
enabling and tough love.

RP: _____

_____

38. Ask the patient's family to
attend the family education
component of the treatment
program.

RP: _____

_____

39. Monitor the patient's family
for enabling behaviors and
redirect them in the family
session as appropriate.

RP: _____

_____

40. Help the patient's family implement and stick with tough love techniques.

    RP: _____

    _____

41. Assign appropriate reading that will increase the family members' knowledge of the disease and recovery process: *Bradshaw on the Family* (Bradshaw); *Adult Children of Alcoholics* (Woititz); *It Will Never Happen to Me* (Black).

    RP: _____

    _____

42. Help family members develop individual relapse-prevention plans for the patient and facilitate a session where plans are shared with the chemically dependent member.

    RP: _____

    _____

__. _____

    _____

    RP: _____

    _____

__. _____

    _____

    RP: _____

    _____

—. _____
_____

RP: _____

_____

DIAGNOSTIC SUGGESTIONS

Axis I:

305.00	Alcohol Abuse
305.70	Amphetamine Abuse
305.20	Cannabis Abuse
305.60	Cocaine Abuse
305.30	Hallucinogen Abuse
305.90	Inhalant Abuse
305.50	Opioid Abuse
305.90	Phencyclidine Abuse
305.40	Sedative, Hypnotic, or Anxiolytic Abuse
305.90	Other (or Unknown) Substance Abuse
303.90	Alcohol Dependence
304.40	Amphetamine Dependence
304.30	Cannabis Dependence
304.20	Cocaine Dependence
304.50	Hallucinogen Dependence
304.60	Inhalant Dependence
304.00	Opioid Dependence
304.90	Phencyclidine Dependence
304.10	Sedative, Hypnotic, or Anxiolytic Dependence
304.90	Other (or Unknown) Substance Dependence
304.80	Polysubstance Dependence
____	_____
____	_____

SUBSTANCE INTOXICATION/WITHDRAWAL

BEHAVIORAL DEFINITIONS

1. Cognitive, behavioral, or emotional changes (alcohol on breath, belligerence, mood lability, impaired cognition, impaired judgment, slurred speech, ataxia) developed shortly after ingestion of or exposure to a substance.
2. Abnormal autonomic reactivity (elevated or decreased vital signs, tachycardia, dilated or constricted pupils, diaphoresis, flushed face, etc.) subsequent to the introduction of a mood-altering substance into the body.
3. Admits to recently abusing a mood-altering chemical.
4. Urine, blood screen, or breathalyzer indicates recent substance use.
5. Psychological symptoms caused by substance withdrawal (e.g., irritability, anxiety, anger, emotional lability, depression, hallucinations, delusions).
6. Intoxication or withdrawal symptoms causing clinically significant impairment in work, school, or play.
7. Preoccupation with strong cravings, leaving treatment, and using mood-altering chemicals.

—. _____

_____

—. _____

_____

—. _____

_____

LONG-TERM GOALS

1. Stabilize condition medically, behaviorally, emotionally, and cognitively and return to functioning within normal parameters.
2. Recover from substance intoxication/withdrawal and participate in a chemical dependency assessment.
3. Understand the severity of the substance use and enter a recovery program.
4. Comply with assessments of substance intoxication and withdrawal.
5. Enter a recovery program necessary to control substance abuse.
6. Understand the extent of the danger to self and others when intoxicated.
7. Understand the reasons for substance intoxication/withdrawal and make plans to resolve the issues that led to use.

—. _____
   _____
—. _____
   _____
—. _____
   _____

SHORT-TERM OBJECTIVES

1. Verbalize acceptance of the need to be in a safe place to recover from substance intoxication/withdrawal. (1, 2, 3)

2. Cooperate with the medical management of substance intoxication/withdrawal. (1, 2, 3)

THERAPEUTIC INTERVENTIONS

1. Welcome the patient to the treatment setting, explain substance intoxication, and describe the procedures that will be used to arrest symptoms.

   RP:*_____

   _____

---

*RP = Responsible Professional

3. Sign a release of information so that the staff can inform significant others about patient's admission and condition. (4)

4. Meet with the physician and take all medications as prescribed. (5, 7)

5. Cooperate with the medical staff during assessments of substance intoxication and possible withdrawal complications. (5, 6, 7)

6. Participate in a biopsychosocial assessment that measures the extent of substance abuse/dependency. (8)

7. Agree to stay with a staff member or treatment buddy during severe intoxication/withdrawal. (9)

8. Report any change in intoxication/withdrawal symptoms to the medical staff. (10)

9. Submit to blood work to confirm that no mood-altering substances are present. (11)

10. Stabilize vital signs within normal parameters. (7, 12)

11. Return cognitive, behavioral, and emotional functioning to preintoxication status. (9, 13, 14)

12. Share the feelings that surround admission for substance intoxication/withdrawal (10, 14)

2. Inform the patient what he/she can expect during intoxication and withdrawal and encourage him/her to cooperate with medical management.

   RP: _____

   _____

3. Teach the patient about the importance of staying in treatment to recover from substance intoxication and possible withdrawal.

   RP: _____

   _____

4. Encourage the patient to sign a release of information so that significant others can be contacted to gain support for the patient's admission to treatment.

   RP: _____

   _____

5. Physician will examine the patient, educate the patient about substance intoxication and withdrawal, order medications as appropriate, titrate medications, and monitor for side effects and effectiveness.

   RP: _____

   _____

6. Medical staff will carry out the orders of the physician, administer medications as directed, and monitor for

13. Verbalize thoughts of harming self or others. (14)

14. Cooperate in reducing environmental stimulation to prevent exacerbation of symptoms. (10, 15)

15. Learn and cooperate with the rules of the facility. (16)

16. Agree to follow through with a personal recovery plan that addresses substance abuse as determined by the biopsychosocial assessment. (17, 18)

___. _____
    _____

___. _____
    _____

___. _____
    _____

side effects and effectiveness.

RP: _____

_____

7. Medical staff will regularly take vital signs and administer the Clinical Institute of Withdrawal Scale, the Narcotic Withdrawal Scale, or equivalent scales, tests, or assessments.

RP: _____

_____

8. Complete a biopsychosocial assessment to determine the extent of the patient's substance abuse and need for treatment.

RP: _____

_____

9. Assign a staff member to remain with the patient until he/she is through intoxication and withdrawal.

RP: _____

_____

10. Teach the patient about the signs and symptoms he/she might experience during substance intoxication and/or withdrawal, then encourage him/her to report any significant change in symptoms to the medical staff.

RP: _____

_____

11. Monitor patient's status via blood tests and report findings in his/her clinical chart.

    RP: _____

    _____

12. Monitor patient's vital signs and report findings to the treatment team.

    RP: _____

    _____

13. Evaluate patient's cognitive, behavioral, and emotional status as detoxification progresses, reporting results to treatment team.

    RP: _____

    _____

14. Probe the feelings that surround substance intoxication, assess danger to self or others, then encourage the patient to report to staff any thoughts of harming self or others.

    RP: _____

    _____

15. Help the patient reduce environment stimulation to a level that will not exacerbate symptoms.

    RP: _____

    _____

16. Teach the patient the rules
of the facility and encourage
him/her to follow the rules
while in treatment.

    RP: _____

    _____

17. Teach the patient that substance withdrawal means
substance dependence, and
then help the patient make
plans for treatment and
recovery.

    RP: _____

    _____

18. Share the results of the
chemical dependency as-
sessment and discuss the
options for substance abuse/
dependence treatment.

    RP: _____

    _____

___. _____

    _____

    RP: _____

    _____

___. _____

    _____

    RP: _____

    _____

___. _____

    _____

    RP: _____

    _____

DIAGNOSTIC SUGGESTIONS

Axis I: 303.00   Alcohol Intoxication
                292.89   Amphetamine Intoxication
                305.90   Caffeine Intoxication
                292.89   Cannabis Intoxication
                292.89   Cocaine Intoxication
                292.89   Hallucinogen Intoxication
                292.89   Opioid Intoxication
                292.89   Phencyclidine Intoxication
                292.89   Sedative, Hypnotic, or Anxiolytic Intoxication
                291.8   Alcohol Withdrawal
                292.0   Amphetamine Withdrawal
                292.0   Cocaine Withdrawal
                292.0   Opioid Withdrawal
                292.0   Sedative, Hypnotic, or Anxiolytic Withdrawal
                292.89   Other (or Unknown) Substance Intoxication
                292.0   Other (or Unknown) Substance Withdrawal

                _____   _____

                _____   _____

SUBSTANCE-INDUCED DISORDERS

BEHAVIORAL DEFINITIONS

1. Memory impairment (amnestic disorder) that persists beyond expected duration of substance intoxication or withdrawal effects.
2. Memory impairment and cognitive disturbance (dementia) that persist beyond expected duration of substance intoxication or withdrawal effects.
3. Unclear awareness of the environment, deficient ability to focus attention, memory dysfunction, language and/or perceptual disturbance (delirium) that developed during or shortly after substance intoxication or withdrawal.
4. Hallucinations or delusions that persist beyond expected duration of substance intoxication or withdrawal effects.
5. Depressed mood that developed during or shortly after substance intoxication or withdrawal.
6. Markedly expansive mood that developed during or shortly after substance intoxication or withdrawal.
7. Prominent anxiety, panic attacks, or obsessions that developed during or shortly after substance intoxication or withdrawal.
8. Sleep disturbance that developed during or shortly after substance intoxication or withdrawal.
9. Sexual dysfunction that developed during or shortly after substance intoxication or withdrawal.

___. _____
    _____

___. _____
    _____

___. _____
    _____

LONG-TERM GOALS

1. Recover from substance-induced disorder and maintain a recovery program free from substance abuse.
2. Improve long- and short-term memory and maintain abstinence from substance abuse.
3. Normalize memory and cognition and maintain abstinence from substance abuse.
4. Recover clear memory and awareness of environment, realistic perceptions, coherent communication, and focused attention and maintain abstinence from substance abuse.
5. End hallucinations and/or delusions and maintain abstinence from substance abuse.
6. Elevate depressed mood to normal and maintain abstinence from substance abuse.
7. Return expansive mood to normal and maintain abstinence from substance abuse.
8. Significantly reduce anxiety symptoms and maintain abstinence from substance abuse.
9. Restore normal sleep patterns and maintain abstinence from substance abuse.
10. Understand the relationship between substance-induced disorder and substance abuse.
11. Participate in medical management of substance-induced disorder and substance abuse.
12. Learn the importance of working a 12-step program to recover from substance-induced disorder and substance abuse.

__. _____

_____

__. _____

_____

__. _____

_____

SHORT-TERM OBJECTIVES

1. Verbalize an acceptance of the need for a safe place in which to receive treatment for the substance-induced disorder and chemical dependence. (1, 2, 3)

2. Verbalize an understanding that the signs and symptoms of the substance-induced disorder are caused by chemical dependence. (2, 3)

3. Verbalize an understanding that the substance-induced disorder is not permanent and will improve if the patient maintains abstinence. (2, 3)

4. Report to staff any thoughts of harming self or others. (4, 5)

5. Verbalize feelings that surround substance-induced disorder and substance abuse. (4, 5, 6)

6. Cooperate with periodic assessments of substance-induced disorder, intoxication, and withdrawal. (5, 6)

7. Cooperate with medical management of the substance-induced disorder. (7, 8)

8. Submit to a physician's physical examination to

THERAPEUTIC INTERVENTIONS

1. Welcome the patient to treatment and explain that he/she is in a safe place. Encourage him/her to stay in treatment long enough to enter recovery.

   RP:*_____

   _____

2. Teach the patient about his/her substance-induced disorder and directly relate signs and symptoms to chemical abuse.

   RP: _____

   _____

3. Teach the patient that his/her symptoms are a direct result of chemical abuse and they will ameliorate if the patient remains abstinent.

   RP: _____

   _____

4. Assess the patient's potential for harming him-/herself or others and take precautionary steps if needed; encourage patient to report to staff any thoughts of harming self or others.

   RP: _____

   _____

_____

*RP = Responsible Professional

assess bodily functions and the need for psychotropic medication. (7, 8)

9. Take prescribed medications as directed by the physician and report symptoms and side effects to the medical staff. (7, 8)

10. Cooperate with a complete psychological assessment and comply with all recommended treatment plans. (9)

11. Take in fluids and nourishment as indicated by the medical staff. (10)

12. Stay with a staff member during severe symptoms of substance-induced disorder, intoxication, or withdrawal. (11)

13. Reduce environmental stimulation to decrease excessive anxiety, perceptual disturbances, and irritability. (12)

14. Talk with a treatment peer who is further along in the program and discuss plans for recovery. (13)

15. Verbalize the need for further treatment and write a plan to address substance-induced disorder and substance abuse. (14, 15)

__. _____

_____

5. Encourage the patient to share his/her feelings surrounding substance-induced disorder and substance abuse.

    RP: _____

    _____

6. As often as necessary, assess the patient with standard instruments such as the Beck Depression Inventory, Beck Anxiety Inventory, Clinical Institute Withdrawal Scale, Narcotics Withdrawal Scale, Mental Status Examination, or Cognitive Screening Capacity Examination.

    RP: _____

    _____

7. Physician will examine the patient, write treatment orders as indicated, titrate medications, and monitor for side effects and effectiveness.

    RP: _____

    _____

8. Medical staff will carry out physician's orders and monitor patient's symptoms and the side effects and effectiveness of the prescribed medication.

    RP: _____

    _____

__.   _____

  _____

__.   _____

  _____

9. Psychologist will complete
a psychological assessment
of the patient and make
recommendations for
treatment.

RP: _____

_____

10. Encourage the patient to
take fluids and nourish-
ment as ordered by the
physician.

RP: _____

_____

11. Assign a staff member to
stay with the patient during
severe substance-induced
disorder, intoxication, or
withdrawal.

RP: _____

_____

12. Adjust the patient's environment until there is mini-
mal stimulation that might
exacerbate excessive anxiety, perceptual distur-
bances, and irritability.

RP: _____

_____

13. Ask treatment peers to
encourage the patient during recovery.

RP: _____

_____

14. Teach the patient about
    12-step recovery and
    encourage him/her to stay
    in treatment.

    RP: _____

    _____

15. Help the patient write a
    plan to treat his/her
    substance-induced disorder
    and substance abuse.

    RP: _____

    _____

__. _____

    _____

    RP: _____

    _____

__. _____

    _____

    RP: _____

    _____

__. _____

    _____

    RP: _____

    _____

DIAGNOSTIC SUGGESTIONS

Axis I: 291.0   Alcohol Intoxication Delirium
291.0   Alcohol Withdrawal Delirium
291.2   Alcohol-Induced Persisting Dementia
291.1   Alcohol-Induced Persisting Amnestic Disorder
291.5   Alcohol-Induced Psychotic Disorder, With Delusions
291.3   Alcohol-Induced Psychotic Disorder, With Hallucinations
291.8   Alcohol-Induced Mood Disorder
291.8   Alcohol-Induced Anxiety Disorder
291.8   Alcohol-Induced Sexual Dysfunction
291.8   Alcohol-Induced Sleep Disorder
291.9   Alcohol-Related Disorder NOS
292.81   Other (or Unknown) Substance-Induced Delirium
292.11   Other (or Unknown) Substance-Induced Psychotic Disorder, With Delusions
292.12   Other (or Unknown) Substance-Induced Psychotic Disorder, With Hallucinations
292.84   Other (or Unknown) Substance-Induced Mood Disorder
292.89   Other (or Unknown) Substance-Induced Anxiety Disorder
292.89   Other (or Unknown) Substance-Induced Sexual Dysfunction
292.89   Other (or Unknown) Substance-Induced Sleep Disorder

_____   _____

_____   _____

SUICIDAL IDEATION

BEHAVIORAL DEFINITIONS

1. Recurrent thoughts of and preoccupation with death.
2. Recurrent or ongoing suicidal ideation without any plans.
3. Ongoing suicidal ideation with a specific plan.
4. Chemical dependency or substance abuse that exacerbates depression, hopelessness, and suicidal ideation.
5. Suicidal and hopeless feelings about life brought on and supported by losses due to substance abuse (financial, familial, vocational, etc.).
6. Belief that others would be better off if he or she were dead.
7. History of suicide attempts.
8. Profound feelings of helplessness, hopelessness, and worthlessness.
9. Recurrent fantasies about joining a significant other lost through suicide or death.
10. Expression of a bleak, hopeless attitude regarding life coupled with recent losses that support this belief (e.g., divorce, death of spouse, illness, loss of job).

__. _____
   _____
__. _____
   _____
__. _____
   _____

LONG-TERM GOALS

1. Resolve preoccupation with death, find new hope, enter a recovery program, and achieve freedom from substance abuse and suicidal ideation.
2. Terminate all suicidal urges, express hope for the future, and continue to abstain from all mood-altering substances.
3. Enter the level of care necessary to protect the patient from his/her suicidal impulses.
4. Understand the relationship between suicidal ideation and substance abuse.
5. Develop a respect for the worth of other addicts and family members.

—. _____
_____
—. _____
_____
—. _____
_____

SHORT-TERM OBJECTIVES

1. Verbalize specific suicidal thoughts, feelings, plans, and actions. (1, 6, 7)

2. Sign a no-harm contract that states the patient will do nothing to harm him-/ herself while in treatment and will contact a staff member if feeling suicidal. (2)

3. Agree to the level of care necessary to protect patient from suicidal impulses (1, 2, 3, 4)

THERAPEUTIC INTERVENTIONS

1. Assess the severity of the suicidal ideation by asking the patient to share suicidal feelings, thoughts, plans, and behaviors.

   RP:* _____

   _____

2. Have the patient sign a no-harm contract that states he/she will do nothing to harm him-/herself while in treatment and will contact

_____

*RP = Responsible Professional

4. Agree to stay with a staff member until suicidal threat resolves. (1, 2, 3, 4)

5. Verbalize an understanding of how suicide risk is magnified by substance abuse. (5, 6)

6. Verbalize the reasons the patient feels helpless, hopeless, and worthless. (1, 6, 7)

7. Identify the losses sustained because of substance abuse. (6, 7)

8. Verbalize feeling important to family members and other addicts in recovery. (8)

9. Meet the physician for an assessment and take all medications as directed. (9, 10)

10. Keep a record of self-defeating thoughts and replace each dysfunctional thought with positive, self-enhancing ideas. (11, 12,)

11. List the reasons that being in treatment for substance abuse gives new hope for the future. (13, 14)

12. List ten reasons for wanting to live (e.g., positive people, places, or things that are a part of the patient's life). (15, 16)

13. Verbalize new hope for resolving interpersonal conflicts through treatment. (17, 18)

a staff member if feeling suicidal.

RP: _____

_____

3. Discuss the levels of care available (locked room, staying with a staff member, transferring to a more intensive level of care, etc.), then decide on the level of care necessary to protect the patient from suicidal impulses.

RP: _____

_____

4. Assign a staff member to stay with the patient until suicidal threat resolves.

RP: _____

_____

5. Help the patient understand how the feelings of shame, loss, and hopelessness are exacerbated by substance abuse.

RP: _____

_____

6. Review the losses (marital, familial, social, legal, financial, health, occupational, etc.) that resulted from substance abuse and led to suicidal hopelessness.

RP: _____

_____

14. Verbalize an understanding of the 12-step attitude of gratitude, then list five things the patient is grateful for each day. Share this with therapist. (19, 20)

15. Verbalize increased hope for the future. (15, 16, 17, 18, 19, 20)

16. Encourage someone else in recovery at least once a day. Record these events and share with therapist. (21, 22)

17. Verbalize an understanding of the 12-step concept of a higher power and discuss how this can be used to recover from suicidal ideation and substance abuse. (23, 24)

18. Practice prayer and meditation at least once each day. (23, 24)

__. _____
   _____

__. _____
   _____

__. _____
   _____

7. Explore the patient's reasons for suicidal ideation and feelings of helplessness, hopelessness, and worthlessness.

   RP: _____

   _____

8. Help the patient understand the meaning behind the AA saying, "what we cannot do alone, we can do together." Help the patient see that other addicts need his/her support in recovery.

   RP: _____

   _____

9. Physician will examine the patient, discuss suicidal ideation and substance abuse, order medications as indicated, titrate medications, and monitor for side effects.

   RP: _____

   _____

10. Staff will administer prescribed medications and monitor for side effects and effectiveness.

   RP: _____

   _____

11. Help patient understand how his/her cognitive messages reinforce hopelessness and helplessness.

   RP: _____

   _____

12. Require patient to keep a daily record of self-defeating thoughts (thoughts of hopelessness, helplessness, worthlessness, catastrophizing, negatively predicting the future, etc.), challenge each thought for accuracy, then replace each dysfunctional thought with one that is positive and self-enhancing.

RP: _____

_____

13. Provide the patient with reasons for new hope in recovery (e.g., being in treatment, working with trained professionals who can act as advocates, receiving encouragement from other addicts, and support from staff members, etc.).

RP: _____

_____

14. Encourage the patient by reminding him/her of the excellent chances for recovery from substance abuse and depression if he/she works the 12-step program.

RP: _____

_____

15. Ask the patient to list ten reasons to live.

RP: _____

_____

16. Have the patient write a
    list of the positive people,
    places, and things in his/
    her life.

    RP: _____

    _____

17. Help the patient see the
    new hope that treatment
    brings to the resolution of
    interpersonal conflicts.

    RP: _____

    _____

18. Meet with patient and sig-
    nificant other with whom
    there is conflict to begin
    conflict resolution.

    RP: _____

    _____

19. Teach the patient about the
    12-step concept of the atti-
    tude of gratitude. Then
    have patient write down
    five things he/she is grate-
    ful for each day.

    RP: _____

    _____

20. Assist patient in developing
    coping strategies for suici-
    dal ideation (e.g., more
    physical exercise, less inter-
    nal focus, increased social
    involvement, and more
    expression of feelings).

    RP: _____

    _____

21. Have the patient read the promises on pages 83 to 84 of the Alcoholics Anonymous *Big Book* and encourage him/her to verbalize hope for the future.

    RP: _____

    _____

22. Require the patient to encourage someone in treatment each day; then record each event and discuss it with the therapist.

    RP: _____

    _____

23. Explain the 12-step concept of a higher power and encourage the patient to ask God for direction each day.

    RP: _____

    _____

24. Have the patient read chapter eleven in AA's *Twelve Steps and Twelve Traditions* (1981); then encourage him/her to pray and meditate at least once each day.

    RP: _____

    _____

___.   _____

    _____

    RP: _____

    _____

—. _____

_____

RP: _____

_____

—. _____

_____

RP: _____

_____

DIAGNOSTIC SUGGESTIONS

Axis I:	291.8	Alcohol-Induced Mood Disorder
	292.84	Amphetamine-Induced Mood Disorder
	292.84	Cocaine-Induced Mood Disorder
	292.84	Inhalant-Induced Mood Disorder
	292.84	Opioid-Induced Mood Disorder
	292.84	Phencyclidine-Induced Mood Disorder
	292.84	Sedative-, Hypnotic-, or Anxiolytic-Induced Mood Disorder
	292.84	Other (or Unknown) Substance-Induced Mood Disorder
	296.xx	Major Depressive Disorder
	300.4	Dysthymic Disorder
	296.xx	Bipolar I Disorder
	296.89	Bipolar II Disorder
	309.xx	Adjustment Disorder
	_____	_____
	_____	_____
Axis II:	301.83	Borderline Personality Disorder
	_____	_____
	_____	_____

TREATMENT RESISTANCE

BEHAVIORAL DEFINITIONS

1. Severe denial of substance dependence in spite of strong evidence of high tolerance, withdrawal symptoms, and many negative consequences of substance abuse.
2. Substitutes a secondary problem as the focus of concern rather than admit that substance abuse is the primary problem.
3. Angry at family members, court, or employer for mandating treatment.
4. Refuses to cooperate with the staff and is at constant risk of leaving treatment against medical advice.
5. Verbally abusive to staff and other patients, frequently irritable, restless, and angry.
6. Dishonest with self and others, believes lies rather than facts regarding his/her chemical abuse.
7. Constantly phones friends or family members to demand they take him/her out of treatment.
8. Refuses to talk to or bond with treatment peers.

—. _____
_____
_____
—. _____
_____
_____
—. _____
_____

LONG-TERM GOALS

1. Accept the truth about the problems caused by substance abuse and enter a recovery program.

2. Accept the powerlessness and unmanageability that substance dependence has brought to his/her life and actively engage in the treatment process.
3. Learn the facts about chemical dependency and make a logical decision about the treatment necessary to arrest addiction.
4. Cooperate with chemical dependence assessments and listen to the diagnosis and treatment plan.
5. Resolve anger at others and accept responsibility for the problems caused by substance abuse and the need for treatment.
6. Resolve interpersonal conflicts with staff and/or other patients and agree to cooperate with treatment.
7. Cooperate with medical management for withdrawal and agree to enter a 12-step recovery program.
8. Be honest with self and others about the extent of the substance abuse and commit to a recovery program.

—. _____

_____

—. _____

_____

—. _____

_____

SHORT-TERM OBJECTIVES

1. Verbalize the reasons for resisting treatment. (1, 2)

2. Share the feelings that surround admission to treatment. (1, 2)

3. Cooperate with biopsychosocial assessment and accept the treatment recommendations of primary therapist. (3, 4, 5)

THERAPEUTIC INTERVENTIONS

1. Probe the reasons the patient is resisting treatment, check for the accuracy of his/her beliefs about substance abuse.

   RP:*_____

   _____

2. Encourage the patient to share the fear, sadness, shame, and anger he/she

---

*RP = Responsible Professional

4. Discuss physical signs and symptoms of excessive and prolonged substance abuse. (3, 4)

5. Listen to the results of the assessments and make a rational informed choice about the treatment needed to arrest addiction. (3, 4, 5)

6. List ten instances when substance abuse led to negative consequences. (6, 7)

7. Sign a release of information so that key family members, friends, employer, and coworkers can be contacted to support his/her treatment. (7, 8)

8. Meet with concerned family members, friends, employer, or coworkers and listen to their concerns about the patient's substance abuse. (7, 8)

9. Sign a release of information so that probation, parole, or court services worker can share information about the patient's treatment. (9)

10. Discuss the reasons for treatment resistance with treatment peers and listen to their feedback. (10, 11)

11. Share plans to leave treatment with peers and staff. (10, 11, 12, 13)

12. Verbalize an understanding of the treatment process. (12)

feels about coming to treatment.

RP: _____

_____

3. Take a biopsychosocial assessment and collect laboratory results and collateral information from friends and relatives. Share the results with the patient.

RP: _____

_____

4. Physician will examine the patient and share the results of the medical history and physical, pointing out signs and symptoms of prolonged and excessive substance abuse.

RP: _____

_____

5. Using the biopsychosocial assessments, help the patient make an informed choice about treatment.

RP: _____

_____

6. Help the patient understand the extent of his/her substance abuse by discussing a number of negative consequences that resulted from chemical use.

RP: _____

_____

13. Stay with a staff member or treatment buddy until the threat of leaving AMA resolves. (13)

14. Discuss the options for treatment and make informed plans to enter treatment in the least-restrictive environment necessary to control addiction. (14)

15. List five lies that were told to hide substance abuse. (15)

16. Write a personal recovery plan that includes the treatment necessary to maintain abstinence. (16)

—. _____
   _____

—. _____
   _____

—. _____
   _____

7. Secure signed releases of information and meet with the patient's employer, family, friends, and/or coworkers to enlist their support for the patient to remain in treatment.

   RP: _____

   _____

8. Request concerned family, friends, employer, coworkers, and others to write letters stating specific instances when the patient's substance abuse hurt them, and share what they are going to do if the patient refuses treatment. Have each person read his/her letter to the patient in a group setting.

   RP: _____

   _____

9. Obtain a release of information and contact the patients' probation, parole, or court services worker to elicit support for treatment.

   RP: _____

   _____

10. Encourage the patient in a group setting to share the reasons he/she does not want to remain in treatment. Facilitate other patients' confrontation of denial and support for the need for treatment.

    RP: _____

    _____

11. Encourage the patient to discuss his/her plans to leave AMA with treatment peers and staff.

    RP: _____

    _____

12. Teach the patient about the treatment process and encourage him/her to stay in treatment as long as necessary to control the substance abuse.

    RP: _____

    _____

13. Assign a staff member or treatment peer to stay with the patient until the risk of leaving treatment AMA resolves.

    RP: _____

    _____

14. Discuss the levels of care available (e.g., recovery group meetings, counseling, outpatient treatment, day treatment, residential treatment, partial hospitalization, and hospitalization) and help the patient make an informed decision about entering treatment.

    RP: _____

    _____

15. Help the patient admit to the lies that he/she told to hide substance abuse.

    RP: _____

    _____

16. Help the patient write a personal recovery plan that includes the treatment necessary to maintain abstinence.

RP: _____

_____

___. _____

_____

RP: _____

_____

___. _____

_____

RP: _____

_____

___. _____

_____

RP: _____

_____

DIAGNOSTIC SUGGESTIONS

Axis I:	305.00	Alcohol Abuse
	305.70	Amphetamine Abuse
	305.20	Cannabis Abuse
	305.60	Cocaine Abuse
	305.30	Hallucinogen Abuse
	305.90	Inhalant Abuse
	305.50	Opioid Abuse
	305.90	Phencyclidine Abuse
	305.40	Sedative, Hypnotic, or Anxiolytic Abuse
	305.90	Other (or Unknown) Substance Abuse
	303.90	Alcohol Dependence
	304.40	Amphetamine Dependence
	304.30	Cannabis Dependence
	304.20	Cocaine Dependence

304.50	Hallucinogen Dependence
304.60	Inhalant Dependence
304.00	Opioid Dependence
304.90	Phencyclidine Dependence
304.10	Sedative, Hypnotic, or Anxiolytic Dependence
304.90	Other (or Unknown) Substance Dependence
304.80	Polysubstance Dependence
_____	_____
_____	_____

Appendix

INDEX OF DSM-IV CODES ASSOCIATED WITH PRESENTING PROBLEMS

Acculturation Problem   **V62.4**
Living-Environment Deficiency
Spiritual Confusion

Acute Stress Disorder   **308.3**
Anxiety
Grief/Loss Unresolved
Posttraumatic Stress

Adjustment Disorder   **309.xx**
Posttraumatic Stress
Suicidal Ideation

Adjustment Disorder With Anxiety   **309.24**
Anxiety
Grief/Loss Unresolved

Adjustment Disorder With Depressed Mood   **309.0**
Depression
Grief/Loss Unresolved

Adjustment Disorder With Disturbance of Conduct   **309.3**
Antisocial Behavior
Grief/Loss Unresolved
Impulsivity
Legal Problems
Peer Group Negativity

Adjustment Disorder With Mixed Anxiety and Depressed Mood   **309.28**
Anxiety
Depression
Grief/Loss Unresolved

Adjustment Disorder With Mixed Disturbance of Emotions and Conduct   **309.4**
Anger
Attention-Deficit/Hyperactivity Disorder
Attention-Deficit/Inattentive Disorder
Grief/Loss Unresolved
Peer Group Negativity

Adult Antisocial Behavior   **V71.01**
Anger
Antisocial Behavior
Family Conflicts
Impulsivity
Legal Problems
Peer Group Negativity

Alcohol Abuse   **305.00**
Substance Abuse/Dependence
Treatment Resistance

Alcohol Dependence   **303.90**
Substance Abuse/Dependence
Treatment Resistance

Alcohol-Induced Anxiety Disorder   291.8
  Anxiety
  Substance-Induced Disorders

Alcohol-Induced Mood Disorder   291.8
  Attention-Deficit/Hyperactivity
    Disorder
  Attention-Deficit/Inattentive
    Disorder
  Substance-Induced Disorders
  Suicidal Ideation

Alcohol-Induced Persisting Amnestic Disorder   291.1
  Substance-Induced Disorders

Alcohol-Induced Persisting Dementia   291.2
  Substance-Induced Disorders

Alcohol-Induced Psychotic Disorder   291.x
  Psychosis

Alcohol-Induced Psychotic Disorder, With Delusions   291.5
  Substance-Induced Disorders

Alcohol-Induced Psychotic Disorder, With Hallucinations   291.3
  Substance-Induced Disorders

Alcohol-Induced Sexual Dysfunction   291.8
  Substance-Induced Disorders

Alcohol-Induced Sleep Disorder   291.8
  Substance-Induced Disorders

Alcohol Intoxication   303.00
  Substance Intoxication/Withdrawal

Alcohol Intoxication Delirium   291.0
  Substance-Induced Disorders

Alcohol-Related Disorder NOS   291.9
  Substance-Induced Disorders

Alcohol Withdrawal   291.8
  Substance Intoxication/
    Withdrawal

Alcohol Withdrawal Delirium   291.0
  Substance-Induced Disorders

Amphetamine Abuse   305.70
  Substance Abuse/Dependence
  Treatment Resistance

Amphetamine Dependence   304.40
  Substance Abuse/Dependence
  Treatment Resistance

Amphetamine-Induced Mood Disorder   292.84
  Suicidal Ideation

Amphetamine Intoxication   292.89
  Substance Intoxication/
    Withdrawal

Amphetamine Withdrawal   292.0
  Substance Intoxication/
    Withdrawal

Antisocial Personality Disorder   301.7
  Anger
  Antisocial Behavior
  Attention-Deficit/Hyperactivity
    Disorder
  Attention-Deficit/Inattentive
    Disorder
  Borderline Traits
  Childhood Trauma
  Family Conflicts
  Impulsivity
  Legal Problems
  Occupational Problems
  Partner Relational Conflicts
  Peer Group Negativity
  Relapse-Prone

Anxiety Disorder NOS   300.00
  Adult Child of an Alcoholic Traits

Attention-Deficit/Hyperactivity Disorder   314
  Impulsivity
  Relapse-Prone

**Child or Adolescent
Antisocial Behavior**   V71.02
  Anger
  Antisocial Behavior
  Family Conflicts
  Impulsivity
  Legal Problems
  Peer Group Negativity

Cocaine Abuse   305.60
  Substance Abuse/Dependence
  Treatment Resistance

Cocaine Dependence   304.20
  Substance Abuse/Dependence
  Treatment Resistance

**Cocaine-Induced Mood
Disorder**   292.84
  Suicidal Ideation

Cocaine Intoxication   292.89
  Substance Intoxication/
    Withdrawal

Cocaine Withdrawal   292.0
  Substance Intoxication/Withdrawal

Conduct Disorder   312.8
  Anger
  Antisocial Behavior
  Attention-Deficit/Hyperactivity
    Disorder
  Attention-Deficit/Inattentive
    Disorder
  Family Conflicts
  Impulsivity
  Legal Problems
  Relapse-Prone

**Conduct Disorder, Adolescent
Onset Type**   312.82
  Peer Group Negativity

Cyclothymic Disorder   301.13
  Depression
  Mania/Hypomania
  Narcissism
  Relapse-Prone

Delirium   293.0
  Medical Issues

Delusional Disorder   297.1
  Psychosis

Dementia   290
  Medical Issues

**Dependent Personality
Disorder**   301.6
  Adult Child of an Alcoholic Traits
  Anxiety
  Borderline Traits
  Childhood Trauma
  Family Conflicts

Depersonalization   300.6
  Posttraumatic Stress

Depressive Disorder NOS   311
  Adult Child of an Alcoholic Traits
  Depression
  Grief-Loss Unresolved
  Occupational Problems

**Disruptive Behavior
Disorder NOS**   312.9
  Attention-Deficit/Hyperactivity
    Disorder
  Attention-Deficit/Inattentive
    Disorder
  Impulsivity

Dissociative Disorder NOS   300.15
  Posttraumatic Stress

**Dissociative Identity
Disorder**   300.14
  Childhood Trauma
  Posttraumatic Stress

Dysthymic Disorder   300.4
  Borderline Traits
  Childhood Trauma
  Depression
  Suicidal Ideation

**Generalized Anxiety
Disorder**   300.02
  Anxiety
  Childhood Trauma
  Occupational Problems

Hallucinogen Abuse   305.30
  Substance Abuse/Dependence
  Treatment Resistance

Schizoid Personality Disorder **301.20**
Partner Relational Conflicts
Relapse-Prone

Schizophrenia **295.xx**
Psychosis

Schizophreniform Disorder **295.40**
Psychosis

Schizotypal Personality Disorder **301.22**
Borderline Traits
Relapse-Prone

Sedative, Hypnotic, or Anxiolytic Abuse **305.40**
Substance Abuse/Dependence
Treatment Resistance

Sedative, Hypnotic, or Anxiolytic Dependence **304.10**
Substance Abuse/Dependence
Treatment Resistance

Sedative-, Hypnotic-, or Anxiolytic-Induced Mood Disorder **292.84**
Suicidal Ideation

Sedative, Hypnotic, or Anxiolytic Intoxication **292.89**
Substance Intoxication/Withdrawal

Sedative, Hypnotic, or Anxiolytic Withdrawal **292.0**
Substance Intoxication/Withdrawal

Separation Anxiety Disorder **309.21**
Anxiety

Sexual Abuse of Adult **V61.1**
Living-Environment Deficiency
Partner Relational Conflicts
Posttraumatic Stress

Sexual Abuse of Child **V61.21**
Living-Environment Deficiency
Posttraumatic Stress

Sexual Abuse of Child (Victim, 995.5) **V61.21**
Childhood Trauma

Sibling Relational Problem **V61.8**
Family Conflicts
Living-Environment Deficiency

Social Phobia **300.23**
Anxiety

Somatization Disorder **300.81**
Medical Issues

Specific Phobia **300.29**
Anxiety

Substance-Induced Anxiety Disorder **292.89**
Anxiety

Substance-Induced Mood Disorder **292.xx**
Attention-Deficit/Hyperactivity Disorder
Attention-Deficit/Inattentive Disorder

Tourette's Disorder **307.23**
Medical Issues

TheraScribe® 3.0 for Windows®

The Computerized Assistant to Psychotherapy Treatment Planning

→ Used in thousands of behavioral health practices and treatment facilities, *TheraScribe® 3.0* is a state-of-the-art Windows®-based treatment planning program which rapidly generates comprehensive treatment plans meeting the requirements of all major accrediting agencies and most third-party payers.

→ In just minutes, this user-friendly program enables you to create customized treatment plans by choosing from thousands of prewritten built-in short-term goals, long-term objectives, therapeutic interventions, automated progress notes, and much more.

→ This networkable software also tracks treatment outcome, stores clinical pathways, and provides ample room for narrative patient histories, treatment summaries, and discharge notes.

→ And best of all, this flexible system can be expanded to include the data in this *Chemical Dependence Treatment Planner.*

✎CHEMICAL DEPENDENCE Upgrade to THERASCRIBE 3.0✐
The behavioral definitions, goals, objectives, and interventions from this *Chemical Dependency Treatment Planner* can be imported into *TheraScribe® 3.0: The Computerized Assistant to Treatment Planning*. For purchase and pricing information, please send in the coupon below.

- -

For more information about *TheraScribe® 3.0* or the *Chemical Dependence Upgrade,* fill in this coupon, and mail it to: M. Fellin, John Wiley & Sons, Inc., 605 Third Avenue, New York, NY 10158

❑ Please send me information on TheraScribe® 3.0
❑ Please send me information on the Chemical Dependence Upgrade to TheraScribe® 3.0

Name _____

Affiliation _____

Address _____

City/State/Zip _____

Phone _____

(🐝)WILEY
Publishers Since 1807

Build your Treatment Planning Library with these time-saving resources from John Wiley & Sons:

WILEY

❋ **The Complete Psychotherapy Treatment Planner (adult disorders)**
176pp ◆ Paper ◆ 0471-11738-2
❋ **The Child and Adolescent Psychotherapy Treatment Planner**
240pp ◆ Paper ◆ 0471-15647-7
❋ **The Continuum of Care Treatment Planner**
208pp ◆ Paper ◆ 0471-19568-5
❋ **TheraScribe® 3.0 for Windows®: *The Computerized Assistant to Psychotherapy Treatment Planning***
Single User/0471-18415-2 ◆ Network/0471-18416-0

And, coming soon...

The Couples Therapy Planner ◆ The Employee Assistance Treatment Planner ◆ The Group Therapy Treatment Planner ◆ The Pastoral Counseling Planner ◆ TheraBiller w/TheraScheduler: *The Mental Health Office Management System*

For more information about on these forthcoming resources, fill in this coupon, and mail it to: M. Fellin, John Wiley & Sons, Inc., 605 Third Avenue, New York, NY 10158

Please send me information on:
❑   The Couples Therapy Treatment Planner
❑   The Employee Assistance Treatment Planner
❑   The Group Therapy Treatment Planner
❑   The Pastoral Counseling Planner
❑   TheraBiller w/TheraScheduler: *The Mental Health Office Management System*

Name _____

Affiliation _____

Address _____

_____

City/State/Zip _____

Phone _____

ABOUT THE DISK

TheraScribe® 3.0 Library Module Installation

The enclosed disk contains files to upgrade your TheraScribe® 3.0 program to include the behavioral definitions, goals, objectives, and interventions from *The Chemical Dependence Treatment Planner*.

Note: You must have TheraScribe® 3.0 for Windows installed on your computer in order to use *The Chemical Dependence Treatment Planner* library module.

To install the library module, please follow these steps:

1. Place the library module disk in your floppy drive.

2. Log in to TheraScribe® 3.0 as the Administrator using the name "Admin" and your administrator password.

3. On the Main Menu, press the "GoTo" button and choose the Options menu item.

4. Press the "Import Library" button.

5. On the Import Library Module screen, choose your floppy disk drive a:\ from the list and press "Go". Note: It may take a few minutes to import the data from the floppy disk to your computer's hard disk.

6. When the installation is complete the library module data will be available in your TheraScribe® 3.0 program.

Note: If you have a network version of TheraScribe® 3.0 installed, you should import the library module one time only. After importing the data, the library module data will be available to all network users.

User Assistance

If you need assistance using this TheraScribe® 3.0 add-on module, call Wiley Technical Support at (212) 850-6753, weekdays beween 9 AM and 4 PM Eastern Standard Time. You can also email Wiley Technical Support at techhelp@wiley.com.

For information on how to install the disk, refer to the **About the Disk** section on page 251.

WILEY
Publishers Since 1807